Fertiliser recommendations

for Agricultural and Horticultural Crops (RB209)

Organic Manures

Arable and forage crops

Vegetables and bulbs

Fruit and hops

Grass

Ministry of Agriculture, Fisheries and Food

Fertiliser Recommendations

for agricultural and horticultural crops

Reference Book **209**

London: The Stationery Office

Sixth Edition 1994
Fifth impression 1999

ISBN 0 11 242935 1

Published by The Stationery Office and available from:

The Publications Centre
(mail, telephone and fax orders only)
PO Box 276, London SW8 5DT
General enquiries 0171 873 0011
Telephone orders 0171 873 9090
Fax orders 0171 873 8200

The Stationery Office Bookshops
123 Kingsway, London WC2B 6PQ
0171 242 6393 Fax 0171 242 6394
68-69 Bull Street, Birmingham B4 6AD
0121 236 9696 Fax 0121 236 9699
33 Wine Street, Bristol BS1 2BQ
0117 926 4306 Fax 0117 929 4515
9-21 Princess Street, Manchester M60 8AS
0161 834 7201 Fax 0161 833 0634
16 Arthur Street, Belfast BT1 4GD
01232 238451 Fax 01232 235401
The Stationery Office Oriel Bookshop
The Friary, Cardiff CF1 4AA
01222 395548 Fax 01222 384347
71 Lothian Road, Edinburgh EH3 9AZ
0131 228 4181 Fax 0131 622 7017

The Stationery Office's Accredited Agents
(see Yellow Pages)

and through good booksellers

FOREWORD

The first comprehensive set of fertiliser recommendations for England and Wales was published by MAFF in the first edition of Bulletin 209, *Fertiliser Recommendations*, in October 1973.

Subsequent revisions were published in 1979, 1983, 1985 and 1988. This revision has been carried out by ADAS and in keeping with previous editions the recommendations are compiled from many sources.

CONTENTS

SECTION 1
FERTILISER RECOMMENDATIONS FOR
AGRICULTURAL AND HORTICULTURAL CROPS

INTRODUCTION

This book gives recommendations for fertiliser use on field crops grown in England and Wales. The recommendations are based on information available from Research and Development carried out by many organisations. Each section of the book covers a particular group of crops and provides advice on how much fertiliser should be applied to a particular type of field. Detailed advice is given on how to reduce rates of mineral fertilisers after taking into account the nutrients available from any organic manures that have been applied. Recommendations on the timing of fertiliser applications are also given for each crop.

WATER PROTECTION (Nitrate and water supply)

Losses of nutrients from agricultural land can pollute both ground and surface waters. The risk of loss by leaching will be greatly reduced by ensuring that the amounts of nitrogen fertiliser applied are no greater than the crop requires and by applying nitrogen in organic manures and fertilisers close to the time when it is needed for crop growth.

Groundwater in Chalk, Limestone and Sandstone aquifers is particularly susceptible to increasing nitrate concentration. These important sources of drinking water react at different rates to changes in nitrate loss from agriculture. It may take several decades for a change in nitrate input from the soil to be fully reflected in the concentration of nitrate in the abstracted water. It is particularly important that fertiliser and organic manure use is carefully assessed in these areas.

CODES OF GOOD AGRICULTURAL PRACTICE

Careful attention to fertiliser recommendations and their accurate field application is an important step towards achieving the right balance between agricultural production and environmental protection. The MAFF Codes of Good Agricultural Practice for the Protection of Water, Air and Soil provide further essential guidance on these wider issues.

The Codes cover all aspects of crop and animal production which affect nutrient losses to water and air.

1

Getting nitrogen fertiliser applications right is important in reducing the amount of nitrate leached but choice of crop, autumn crop cover, cultivations, organic manure use and grassland management all have a major impact on the quantity of nitrate lost. Accurate records of past fertiliser use and the regular calibration of fertiliser spreading machinery will increase the accuracy with which fertiliser use is determined and fertilisers are spread.

NITROGEN

The recommendations are those that will give the best financial return based on current prices of produce and fertilisers. This will always be obtained with less fertiliser than is needed to give maximum yield. Increases in crop yield from applied nitrogen fertiliser become less as the amount of nitrogen fertiliser is increased. Above a certain point the value of extra crop produced is less than the cost of nitrogen fertiliser needed to produce it. For example recommendations for cereals are based on a fertiliser cost:grain price ratio of 3:1. Gross margins will be improved if adequate allowance is made for nitrogen provided by the soil. This depends mainly on soil type, previous cropping and organic manure use. It requires substantial changes in the value of a crop or the cost of fertiliser to alter the recommendations.

Each section of the book explains how to assess these nitrogen contributions when working out the amount of fertiliser nitrogen that should be applied to a particular field for a particular group of crops.

Timing

Correct timing of nitrogen fertiliser applications is equally important to ensure that crops make the maximum use of the nitrogen that is applied and of that which is released from the soil. For example, there is no benefit from applying autumn nitrogen to winter cereal crops because nitrogen uptake is small during the autumn and winter and the supply from soil reserves is adequate. Details of timing of applications are given for each crop.

Organic Manures

Field application of organic manures, whether animal manures or sewage sludges, are a major source of nitrogen for crops, but a major source of uncertainty in working out how much fertiliser nitrogen is required. The nitrogen supply from organic manure is the most difficult factor for farmers and growers to assess accurately. Fields given organic manures either as the only fertiliser or in combination with inorganic fertiliser generally have larger losses of nitrogen to air and to water compared with fields given only inorganic fertiliser. The best available information for assessing the nitrogen contribution from organic manures is given in this book. Careful attention to nutrient content, amount and timing of application of organic manures will minimise the amount of inorganic fertiliser needed and losses of nitrogen to air and water.

Soil sampling and analysis

Recent UK work has compared different systems of producing nitrogen fertiliser recommendations. The use of soil sampling to 90 cm and analysis for mineral nitrogen (ammonium and nitrate nitrogen) has been compared with systems based on calculation of soil reserves from previous crop and fertiliser history as used here. The soil mineral nitrogen technique is recommended where estimates of soil nitrogen reserves are large and uncertain. It is of particular value where a field has a history of frequent organic manure applications. For other situations, the procedures recommended in this book have been shown to be equal to or more reliable than soil mineral nitrogen analysis.

PHOSPHORUS, POTASSIUM, MAGNESIUM AND SULPHUR

To allow efficient uptake and utilisation of nitrogen, crops need to be adequately supplied with other nutrients from soil reserves, fertilisers or organic manures. Soil pH must also be maintained at an appropriate level. To ensure the efficient use of phosphate, potash and magnesium fertilisers, application rates should be based on soil analysis. The recommendations are to be used in conjunction with the results of soil analysis carried out by standard laboratory methods (see MAFF ADAS Reference Book 427, *The analysis of agricultural materials*). This analysis is only meaningful if performed on an adequate and representative soil sample. Under most cropping systems, soil nutrient status changes slowly and it is safe to use soil analysis results as a basis for fertiliser recommendations for up to 4 years from the date of sampling. After 4 years a new analysis should be made.

Soil analysis reports usually give the quantity of available phosphorus (P) and potassium (K) in terms of milligrams per litre of soil (mg/l). These amounts are also expressed as Indices (see Appendix 1). These Indices indicate the relative amounts of nutrients in the soil that are available to the crop, and range from 0 (deficient) to 9 (very large). If soil nutrient reserves are small, recommendations are calculated to meet crop requirement and to leave a residue that will build soil reserves and increase soil fertility. Where moderate amounts of nutrients are present in the soil, fertiliser applications are recommended to balance crop offtake and hence maintain soil nutrient levels. No application is recommended where soil nutrient reserves are large.

Recommendations for soils at Index 0 and 1 are for the mid-point of the range of soil reserves covered by those indices. Where soil analysis is reported in mg/l and shows that those reserves are substantially above or below the mid-point of Index 0 or 1 fertiliser addition may be adjusted accordingly.

Maintenance recommendations are based on the amounts of phosphate, potash and magnesium removed by typical crops. Where yields are substantially different from those used here it may be appropriate to use larger or smaller amounts of phosphate, potash, magnesium or sulphur.

Account should always be taken of the nutrients available for crop growth from any organic manures applied. The amount and availability of phosphate, potash, magnesium and sulphur will depend upon the amount and type of manure used. On many fields, additional inorganic fertiliser to supply phosphate, potash, magnesium and sulphur will not be required. Particular care should be taken to avoid the build up of excessive levels of phosphorus in soil as this will contribute to increased phosphorus in run-off water reaching streams and rivers. This can be a particular risk where slurry or organic manures are applied to fields adjacent to waterways, especially if the soil is waterlogged or frozen.

Recommendations for magnesium are given as kg/ha of magnesium oxide (MgO) and for sulphur as the oxide (SO_3). Previous editions gave the recommendations as kg/ha of Mg or S. This enables easier calculation of the amount of fertiliser needed as the Fertiliser Regulations require magnesium fertiliser content to be expressed as MgO and sulphur fertiliser contents as SO_3.

Organic manures

SECTION 2
ORGANIC MANURES

Organic manures (farmyard manure [FYM], poultry manures, slurries and sewage sludges) are valuable sources of organic matter and of the major nutrients: nitrogen, phosphate, potash and sulphur. They also contain magnesium and trace elements. Taking account of these nutrients can often result in considerable savings in inorganic fertiliser use. However, organic manures can also present a considerable environmental risk if not used carefully. Guidance on avoiding pollution is given in the MAFF Codes of Good Agricultural Practice.

FERTILISER PLANNING AND ORGANIC MANURES

For reliable fertiliser planning it is essential that both the nutrient content, rate and time of application of manures are known.

The nutrient content and total output of animal excreta from a livestock unit can be greatly influenced by factors such as diet, the amount and composition of litter, and dilution by water. The available nitrogen content of manures will also depend on the time of year when the manure is spread and the method of application.

Table 1 (page 8) is a guide to the amounts of nutrients in animal manures. The 'typical' nutrient contents are based on the average analysis of large numbers of samples.

Organic manures contain significant quantities of sulphur and have been shown to be effective sulphur fertilisers in responsive areas. When applied at 50 m^3/ha, cattle slurry will typically supply 25–38 kg/ha available sulphur as SO_3 which may be sufficient for one cut of silage.

For a particular livestock unit, the nutrient content of the manure produced may be quite different from the values given in Table 1, yet be fairly consistent over several years. It is therefore worthwhile having the nutrient content of a representative sample determined by analysis once or twice a year. For slurries these results can be supplemented by interim assessments using a slurry hydrometer or slurry nitrogen meter. Such on-farm monitoring is particularly useful where liquid is separated by a weeping wall store, strainer box or mechanical separator. The nutrient content of such liquids is greatly dependent upon dilution.

Chemical analyses usually measure the total quantities of nutrients in organic manures. The effectiveness or availability of these nutrients for crop uptake must be assessed before the fertiliser equivalent of the manure can

Table 1   Typical nutrient content of animal manures

	DM %	Total Nutrients			Available Nutrients[1]		
		Nitrogen	Phosphate	Potash	Nitrogen	Phosphate	Potash
Fresh FYM[2]			kg/t			kg/t	
Cattle	25	6.0	3.5	8.0	See	2.1	4.8
Pig	25	7.0	7.0	5.0	Table 2	4.2	3.0
Poultry manures			kg/t			kg/t	
Layer manure	30	15	13	9.0	See	7.8	6.8
Broiler/ turkey litter	60	29	25	18	Table 2	15	14
Slurries			kg/m³			kg/m³	
Dairy[3]	6	3.0	1.2	3.5	See	0.60	3.2
Beef[3]	6	2.3	1.2	2.7	Table 2	0.60	2.4
Pig[3]	6	5.0	3.0	3.0		1.5	2.7
Separated cattle slurries (liquid)			kg/m³			kg/m³	
Strainer box	1.5	1.5	0.25	2.2	See	0.12	2.0
Weeping wall	3	2.0	0.50	3.0	Table 2	0.25	2.7
Mechanical separator	4	3.0	1.2	3.5		0.60	3.2

Notes:
(1) Nutrients that are available for utilisation by the next crop.
(2) Values of Nitrogen and Potash will be lower for FYM stored in the open or for long periods.
(3) It is common for farm slurries to contain approximately 6% DM. Slurries of DM% other than 6% will have greater or lesser concentrations of nutrients than those shown above. Undiluted slurry will usually contain approximately 10% DM.

Conversion factors
multiply kg/m³ by 9 to give units/1000 gallons
multiply kg/t by 2 to give units/ton

be calculated. Values for the availability of the nitrogen, (Table 2, page 9) phosphate and potash (Table 1) in manures have been assessed by field experimentation.

LIVESTOCK WASTE PRODUCTION AND GOOD AGRICULTURAL PRACTICE

The quantity of animal manures produced on a farm depends on a number of factors including the number and type of livestock, the diet and feeding

Table 2 Percentage of total nitrogen available to the next crop following applications of animal manures (% of total nitrogen).

Timing		Autumn (Aug–Oct)[1]		Winter (Nov–Jan)		Spring (Feb–April)	Summer use on grassland
Soil type	DM (%)	Sandy/ shallow	Other[3] mineral	Sandy/ shallow	Other[3] mineral	All soils	All soils[2]
Surface application							
Fresh FYM[4]	25	5	5	10	15	20	n/a
Poultry manures	30–60	10	15	15	25	35	n/a
Dairy/beef slurries[5]	6	5	10	10	20	30	20
Pig slurry[5]	6	5	10	10	25	35	20
Separated slurries[5]	1–4	5	10	15	30	50	35
Rapid incorporation/injection[6]							
Fresh FYM[4]	25	5	10	10	15	25	n/a
Layer manure	30	10	15	15	30	50	n/a
Broiler/turkey manure	60	10	15	15	25	40	n/a
Dairy/beef slurries	2–10	5	10	15	30	50	
Pig slurry	2–10	5	10	15	35	60	

Notes:
(1) Where average or actual excess winter rainfall is significantly below (annual total rainfall 750 mm), the values for autumn application sh increased to those given for winter application which assume 150 r rainfall after application.
(2) The yield response to summer applications can be very variable ac soil and weather conditions. Later applications (July/August) are lik less effective.
(3) Excluding deep silty and clay soils where nitrate leaching losses ar be less. The % total nitrogen available to the next crop will be grea
(4) Values should be reduced by up to half for FYM materials that have stored in the open or for long periods.
(5) Ammonia loss decreases the more dilute the slurry. The % of total nitrogen available to the next crop will therefore depend upon slurry dry matter, being greater for dilute slurries.
(6) The yield response of grass injected with slurries will depend on the extent of injector tine damage to the sward. Values shown for May–June injection assume good soil conditions; utilisation of nitrogen from later timings or injection in dry conditions will be less.

9

system, the volume of dirty water and rainwater entering storage facilities, and the amount of bedding used.

Although the volume of manure to be managed will vary considerably with the amount of water introduced into the system, guideline quantities for the output of excreta, based upon standard moisture contents, are useful for planning manure management systems (Table 3, below).

It is often useful to estimate the total output of nutrients (Table 4, page 11) during the housing period based on the guideline outputs of excreta and the typical nutrient contents. These values will tend to be less variable than output volumes because they do not vary with dilution.

Table 3   Quantity of excreta produced by livestock during housing period

Type of livestock	Body weight (kg)	Dry matter (%)	Typical output (kg/day)	Housing period (% of year)	Quantity per year (t or m³)
Dairy cow	550	10	57	50	10.4
Dairy cow	450	10	44	50	8.0
Dairy cow (FYM)	550	25	37[1]	50	6.7[1]
Beef bullock	400	10	27	50	4.9
Beef bullock (FYM)	400	25	33[2]	50	6.0[2]
Dry sow	90–120	10	4.0	83	1.2
Lactating sow and piglets	90–120	10	12	17	0.8
Sow and piglets (FYM)	90–120	25	6.7	100	2.4
Weaner	5–20	10	1.5	18	0.1
Pig, dry meal fed	20–90	10	4.0	94	1.4
Pig, liquid fed (water:meal ratio 4:1)	20–90	6	7.0	94	2.4
Pig, whey fed	20–90	3	14	94	4.8
Pig, dry meal (FYM)	20–90	25	4.4	94	1.5
1000 laying hens	2000	30	115	100	42
1000 broilers[3]	2700	60	73	78	21
1000 turkeys (male)[4]	13500[5]	60	159	77[6]	44.5
1000 turkeys (female)[4]	7200[5]	60	74	77[6]	20.8

Notes:
(1) Assumes 50% of excreta on bedded area. 50% of excreta will be produced as slurry which is excluded.
(2) Assumes all excreta goes to bedded area during housing period.
(3) Assumes 1.0 kg litter per bird per crop.
(4) Assumes 4.8 kg litter per bird per crop.
(5) Finishing weight of birds.
(6) Assumes 2 crops of birds per year.

Table 4 Estimated quantities of nutrients produced in animal manures during housing (quantity of total nutrients).

	Housing period (% of year)	Nitrogen	Phosphate (kg)	Potash
1 Dairy cow (550 kg)[1]	50	47	21	52
1 Dairy cow (450 kg)[1]	50	36	16	40
1 Beef bullock[1]	50	17	10	19
1 Sow plus piglets[1]	100	14	10	8.0
1 Fattening pig[1]	94	10	7.0	5.5
1000 laying hens	100	630	545	380
1000 broilers	78	610	525	380
1000 male turkeys	77	1290	1110	800
1000 female turkeys	77	605	520	375

Notes:

(1) Values calculated using typical nutrient concentrations at 10% DM.
Conversion factor:
Multiply kg by 2 to give units.

The Code of Good Agricultural Practice for the Protection of Water (MAFF, 1991) recommends that the amount of total nitrogen in organic manures spread on land should not exceed 250 kg/ha/year. Lesser amounts than this may be appropriate in sensitive catchments or where crop nutrient requirement is small.

UTILISATION OF MANURES FOR CROP PRODUCTION

Some of the nutrients in organic manures are in a form readily available to be taken up by crops during the growing season following application. For nitrogen this approximates to the soluble N component—ammonium N (NH_4-N) in slurries and ammonium and uric acid N in poultry manures. The nitrogen that is not readily available can remain in the soil, increase nutrient reserves, become available to crops in later seasons and be at risk of leaching.

In order to make optimum use of the nitrogen in organic manures, the manure should be applied as close as possible to the time when maximum crop growth and nitrogen uptake occur. The nitrogen value of manures will generally be considerably reduced if applied in autumn or early winter due to losses of nitrogen by leaching (more important on sandy or shallow soils) or denitrification ie loss in gaseous form (mainly heavy soils). Opportunities can occur in late winter or early spring. Wherever possible, applications for spring-sown crops should be delayed until after Christmas.

11

Table 5 Estimated amount of available nitrogen for the next crop following applications (10 t/ha or 10 m³/ha) of animal manures (based on typical nitrogen contents).

Timing		Autumn (Aug–Oct)[1]		Winter (Nov–Jan)		Spring (Feb–April)	Summer use on grassland
Soil type	DM (%)	Sandy/ shallow	Other mineral[2]	Sandy/ shallow	Other mineral[3]	All soils	All soils[2]
SURFACE APPLICATION				kg/10t			
Fresh FYM[4]							
Cattle	25	3.0	3.0	6.0	9.0	12	n/a
Pig	25	3.5	3.5	7.0	11	14	n/a
Poultry manures				kg/10t			
Layer manure	30	15	23	23	38	53	n/a
Broiler/ turkey litter	60	29	44	44	73	102	n/a
Slurries[5]				kg/10m³			
Dairy	6	1.5	3.0	3.0	6.0	9.0	6.0
Beef	6	1.0	2.5	2.5	4.5	7.0	4.5
Pig	6	2.5	5.0	5.0	13	18	10.0
Separated slurries				kg/10m³			
Strainer box	1–4	1.0	1.5	2.0	4.5	7.5	5.0
Weeping wall	1–4	1.0	2.0	3.0	6.0	10	7.0
RAPID INCORPORATION/INJECTION[6]				kg/10t			
Fresh FYM[4]							
Cattle	25	3.0	6.0	6.0	9.0	15	n/a
Pig	25	3.5	7.0	7.0	11	18	n/a
Poultry manures				kg/10t			
Layer manure	30	15	23	23	45	75	n/a
Broiler/ turkey litter	60	29	43	43	73	116	n/a
Slurries				kg/10m³			
Dairy	6	1.5	3.0	4.5	9.0	15	15
Beef	6	1.0	2.5	3.5	7.0	12	12
Pig	6	2.5	5.0	8	18	30	30

Notes:

(1) Where average or actual excess winter rainfall is significantly below 250 mm (annual rainfall 750 mm), the values for autumn application should be increased to those given for winter application which assume 150 mm excess rainfall after application.

(2) The yield response to summer applications can be very variable according to soil and weather conditions. Later applications (July/August) are likely to be less effective.

(3) Excluding deep silty and clay soils where nitrate leaching losses are likely to be less. The % total nitrogen available to the next crop will be greater.

(4) Values should be reduced by up to half for FYM materials that have been stored in the open or for long periods.

(5) Ammonia loss decreases as slurries are diluted. The % of total nitrogen available to the next crop will therefore depend upon slurry dry matter, being greater for dilute slurries.

(6) The yield response of grass injected with slurries will depend on the extent of injector tine damage to the sward. Values shown for May–June injection assume good soil conditions; utilisation of nitrogen from later timings or injection in dry conditions will be less.

Conversion factors:
multiply kg/10 m³ by 0.9 to give units/1000 gallons
multiply kg/10 t by 2 to give units/10 ton

Ammonia volatilisation is a major route of nitrogen loss. Losses are greatest from high dry matter slurry and where manures are left on the soil surface after application. Rapid incorporation or injection within a few hours of application will reduce ammonia losses and increase the fertiliser value of the manure.

Estimates of the percentage of the total nitrogen remaining available for spring growth following different timings of manure applications are given in Table 2. Values in terms of kg/10tonne and kg/10m³ are given in Table 5.

Following dry winters, it is likely that the nitrogen content of autumn/winter applied manures will be significantly greater than average and the correction shown in footnote 1 of Table 5 should be followed. Appropriate adjustments to spring fertiliser nitrogen recommendations should be made.

The soluble nitrogen component of straw-based cattle and pig manures is less than that of slurries or poultry manure. For autumn-sown crops, these materials may be applied and incorporated before sowing with less risk of significant nitrogen losses over winter by leaching or denitrification than might occur from autumn application of slurries. For spring-sown crops application in late winter or early spring is preferred.

13

A large part of the nitrogen in organic manures is not taken up by the crop in the season following application and will accumulate in soil organic matter. This nitrogen will be gradually released over many years and may allow further savings in nitrogen fertiliser. Where organic manures are applied every year or where large amounts are applied frequently it can be worthwhile having soils sampled to depth and analysed for mineral nitrogen.

For phosphate and potash, where soil analysis shows little nutrient reserve (Index 0 or 1) or where responsive crops are to be grown, eg potatoes or vegetables, only the readily available phosphate and potash in manures should be taken into account when calculating fertiliser requirement. The remainder will accumulate in soil and in time will reduce the amount of annual fertiliser needed. Where soil reserves are moderate to large (Index 2 and above) fertiliser dressings can be reduced by the quantity of total phosphate and potash applied in manures. For particularly responsive crops, reduce fertiliser dressings by the amounts of available nutrients applied in manures even at higher soil Indices.

Slurry application to growing crops

The nitrogen in slurries may be used more efficiently if dilute slurries (less than 4% DM) are applied to arable crops in spring. Slurry applied at this time has been shown to be a much more efficient and reliable source of nitrogen. To maximise benefits and to minimise environmental problems, slurries and manures should be applied evenly. To minimise the risk of crop scorch, applications should not be made to cereal crops after the first node stage. Specialist equipment is available to spread slurries using tramlines. The maximum rate used will depend upon the available nitrogen content and dilution. A good guide is to apply no more than 2/3 of the crop nitrogen fertiliser requirement as available slurry nitrogen. This guide also applies to all other uses of manure.

Utilisation of organic manures for grassland

Losses by leaching of nitrogen from organic manures applied to grassland in winter or early spring are likely to be less than for similar dressings on arable land. The nitrogen efficiency of manures or slurries applied in early summer, eg after first cut silage, is likely to be low due to losses of ammonia and may also cause smothering or scorching of the crop.

SEWAGE SLUDGE

Sewage sludges are useful fertilisers and soil conditioners. When they are applied to agricultural land, the Sludge (Use in Agriculture) Regulations

Table 6   Typical nitrogen and phosphate analysis of sewage sludges (as spread)

Sludge Type		Nitrogen		Phosphate	
	DM %	Total %	Availability[1] %	Total %	Availability[1] %
Liquid undigested	5	0.18	35	0.15	50
Liquid digested	4	0.20	100% of[2] NH_4^+–N + 15% organic N	0.15	50
Undigested cake	25	0.75	20	0.65	50
Digested cake	25	0.75	15	0.90	50

Notes:
(1) Percentage available in the growing season following spring application.
(2) If ammonium N analysis is not provided, assume 60% of total N is available.

Table 7   Total and available nutrients in sludge (as spread)

Sludge Type	Total		Available[1]	
	Nitrogen	Phosphate	Nitrogen	Phosphate
Liquid undigested (kg/m^3)	1.8	1.5	0.6	0.8
Liquid digested (kg/m^3)	2.0	1.5	1.2	0.8
Sludge cake (undigested) (kg/t)	7.5	6.5	1.5	3.2
Sludge cake (digested) (kg/t)	7.5	9.0	1.1	4.5

Notes:
(1) Nutrients that are available from a spring application for utilisation by the next crop.

(1990) and Code of Practice for Agricultural Use of Sewage Sludge must be followed. These require that applications match the fertiliser needs of the crops, that unacceptable concentrations of heavy metals do not accumulate in soils and crops and that disease risks to humans and livestock are minimised. Sludges vary in their composition. Information available from the supplier will enable the nutrient value to be assessed. Tables 6–8 (pages 15–16) give a guide to the typical nutrient value of sludges, based on analyses of a large number of samples.

Available nitrogen from an autumn application will be greater after a cold, dry winter than after a mild, wet one. The availability of nitrogen from surface-applied sludge assumes a typical dry matter content of 4%. If the

Table 8 Percentage of total nitrogen available to the next crop following applications of sewage sludges (% of total N).

Timing		Autumn (Aug–Oct)[1]		Winter (Nov–Jan)		Spring[2] (Feb–April)	Summer use on grassland
Soil type	DM (%)	Sandy/ shallow	Other mineral	Sandy/ shallow	Other mineral	All soils	All soils[2]
Sludge type							
Liquid digested	4	5	10	15	35	60	40
Digested cakes	25	5	5	10	15	15	n/a

Notes:

(1) Where average or actual winter rainfall is significantly below 250 mm (annual rainfall 750 mm) the values for autumn application should be increased to those given for winter application which assume 150 mm excess winter rainfall after application.

(2) Following injection or rapid incorporation, ammonia volatilisation losses will be reduced and nitrogen utilisation may be improved. Grass yield response will depend on the extent of injector tine damage to the sward.

sludge is substantially thickened before application the percentage of nitrogen that is available may be reduced. Although injection of liquid sludge reduces losses by ammonia volatilisation, the benefit on grassland is difficult to predict and is dependent upon the extent of injector tine damage to the sward. As with animal manures, the availability of nitrogen in sewage sludge, particularly liquid digested sludge, will vary with the time and method of application (Table 7).

Pollution

Spreading organic manures between late winter and April rather than in the autumn provides a more reliable basis for making reductions in the use of fertiliser nitrogen and will reduce pollution from nitrate leaching. Moreover by taking account of the readily available nitrogen in animal manures and reducing fertiliser nitrogen accordingly, the potential for nitrogen loss will be further reduced.

Spreading organic manures may cause the loss of ammonia to the atmosphere. Manures and slurries must be incorporated within 24 hours to minimise ammonia loss. Injection of slurry or sludge into soil will reduce ammonia loss and will increase the amount of nitrogen available for crop growth (see Table 2).

16

There is little leaching of phosphate or potash following spreading of organic manures at recommended rates as any phosphate or potash not immediately used by plants is absorbed by the soil. Over-application on sandy soils for many years can lead to potentially damaging accumulation in soils, particularly if the soil becomes saturated with phosphate. Care should be taken to minimise the risk of run-off of phosphorus into surface waters. Phosphorus may also enter water courses if slurries are applied to land when soil surface layers are dry and cracked above the permeable fill over drains.

Example 1
50 m³/ha dairy slurry at 6% dry matter are applied in mid-December to the surface of a grass field to be cut for silage.

Grass: 3rd year after reseeding
Ley/arable rotation
Annual nitrogen use: 200 kg/ha
Nitrogen reserves: moderate

Soil: P Index 1
K Index 1

NITROGEN
Total amount of nitrogen applied (from Table 1)
= 50 (m³/ha) $\times$ 3.0 (kg/m³) = 150 kg/ha
Amount likely to remain available for spring growth (from Table 2)
= 150 kg/ha $\times$ 20% = *30 kg/ha*

PHOSPHATE AND POTASH
Amounts of available phosphate and potash (from Table 1)
Phosphate = 50 (m³/ha) $\times$ 0.6 (kg/m³) = *30 kg/ha*
Potash = 50 (m³/ha) $\times$ 3.2 (kg/m³) = *160 kg/ha*

	Nitrogen	Phosphate	Potash
Recommendations for first-cut silage, 68–70D, (Pages 106 & 107) kg/ha	120	60	100
Less nutrients available from slurry kg/ha	30	30	160
Nutrients to be supplied as fertiliser kg/ha	*90*	*30*	*0*

Example 2

8 t/ha broiler manure applied and immediately ploughed in before planting
maincrop potatoes
  Soil loamy sand
  P Index 4
  K Index 1

NITROGEN

Total amount of nitrogen applied (from Table 1)
  8 (t/ha) × 29 (kg/t) = 232 kg/ha
Amount likely to remain available for spring growth (from Table 2)
  = 232 (kg/ha) × 40% = 93 kg/ha

PHOSPHATE AND POTASH

Amounts of available phosphate and potash (from Table 1)
  Phosphate = 8 (t/ha) × 15 = 120 kg/ha
  Potash = 8 (t/ha) × 14 = 112 kg/ha

	Nitrogen	Phosphate	Potash
Recommendations for maincrop potatoes (page 40) kg/ha	240	100	300
Less nutrients available from broiler manure kg/ha	93	120	112
Nutrients needed to be supplied as fertiliser kg/ha	*147*	*0*	*188*

Arable and forage crops

SECTION 3
ARABLE AND FORAGE CROPS

SOIL SAMPLING

The results of a soil analysis are only as good as the sample on which they are based. To give meaningful results, a soil sample must be representative of the area sampled and taken to a uniform depth (normally 15 cm). Uniformity of sampling depth is particularly important where crops are established without ploughing.

Areas of land known to differ in some important respects (eg soil type, previous cropping, applications of manure, fertiliser or lime) should be sampled separately. Small areas known to differ from the majority of a field should be excluded from the sample. A sample of 25 individual sub-samples (cores) will be adequate for a uniform area. The sub-sample points must be selected systematically, with an even distribution over the whole area. This may be achieved by following the pattern of a letter 'W' and taking sub-samples at regular intervals. When doing this, avoid headlands and the immediate vicinity of hedges and trees or other unusual features. On soils where acidity is known to occur, spot testing with soil indicator over the whole area will indicate if acidity is present in patches. This can occur in areas where soils generally contain free lime.

Under most arable cropping systems, soil nutrient levels other than inorganic N change slowly so it is not necessary to resample and analyse every year. In general, sampling every fourth year is satisfactory as a basis for fertiliser recommendations, but pH may need more frequent monitoring.

SOIL ACIDITY AND LIMING

The soil pH is a measure of acidity or alkalinity and ranges from about 4.0 (very acid), when most crops will fail, to about 8.0 for soils which are naturally rich in lime or have been over-limed.

Although grasses and some crops such as rye and potatoes can tolerate more acid soil conditions than others such as barley and sugar beet, it is necessary to maintain the soil at a pH suitable for the rotation.

For most arable rotations, the soil pH should he maintained at 6.5 for mineral soils and 5.8 for peaty soils.

Where the occasional cereal crop other than barley is grown in a predominately grassland rotation the soil pH need only be raised to 6.0. If the cereal is barley the pH should be 6.2.

The lime requirement of an acid soil is assessed and reported in tonnes per hectare (t/ha) of ground limestone or ground chalk. The amount of lime recommended for soils of the same pH may vary depending on soil texture and organic matter content.

The value quoted on a soil analysis report for an arable rotation is usually the amount of lime required to maintain a 20 cm depth of soil at pH 6.5. Where soil is known to be acid to a depth greater than 20 cm a proportionately greater quantity of lime should be applied. Where dressings in excess of 12 t/ha are required, half should be deeply cultivated into the soil and ploughed down with the remainder applied to the surface and then worked in. Although recommendations are quoted in terms of ground limestone or ground chalk, other forms of lime can be used provided the rate of application is adjusted to take account of differences in neutralising value (NV).

Any lime needed should be applied well before sowing or planting. Because it can take some months for lime to correct soil acidity it is unwise to grow a crop which is sensitive to acidity immediately after liming a very acid field.

Over-liming should be avoided, particularly on sandy and peaty soils, as it can induce deficiencies of trace elements such as manganese and boron.

PLANT NUTRIENTS

Nitrogen

Measurement of mineral nitrogen in the soil to 90 cm depth is recommended where nitrogen residues are expected to be large. (Soil sampling and analysis, page 3). Nitrogen recommendations in other situations are usually based on an assessment of crop requirement and soil nitrogen supply. The Index system described below uses the expected residues from previous crops to assess the available nitrogen in the soil.

There are three soil nitrogen Indices. Fields in Index 0 have small nitrogen reserves and more nitrogen fertiliser is required compared with fields in Index I. Index 2 soils have the greatest soil nitrogen reserves.

Usually it is only necessary to consider the last crop grown to determine the field's nitrogen Index, but after lucerne, long leys and permanent pasture it is necessary to consider histories longer than one year. Previous dressings of animal manures should also be taken into account.

Nitrogen Index based on last crop grown

Index 0	Index 1	Index 2
Cereals Sugar beet	Potatoes Oilseed rape	Any crop in field receiving large frequent dressings of FYM or slurry
Vegetables receiving less than 200 kg/ha N	Vegetables receiving more than 200 kg/ha N	Lucerne
Forage crops removed	Forage crops grazed	Long leys, grazed or cut and grazed receiving more than 250 kg/ha N or with high clover content
Set-aside (rotational)		
Leys (1–2 year) grazed or cut and grazed, low N	Leys (1–2 year) grazed or cut and grazed, high N	Any managed permanent pasture
Leys (1–2 year) cut only	Long leys, cut only	
Permanent pasture poor quality matted	Long leys, grazed or cut and grazed, low N	

Low N less than 250 kg/ha nitrogen per year and small clover content.
High N more than 250 kg/ha nitrogen per year or large clover content.

Some crops such as peas and beans leave intermediate residues and should be regarded as being part way between Index 0 and Index I.

To find the nitrogen Index of a field look up the last crop grown in the table above. If lucerne, a long ley or permanent pasture has been grown during the last five years, look up the Index in the next table and use the higher of the two values.

23

Nitrogen Index—following lucerne, long leys and permanent pasture

	1st crop	2nd crop	3rd crop	4th crop	5th crop
Lucerne	2	2	1	0	0
Long leys cut only	1	1	0	0	0
Long leys grazed or cut and grazed, low N	1	1	0	0	0
Long leys grazed or cut and grazed, high N	2	2	1	0	0
Permanent pasture poor quality, matted	0	0	0	0	0
Permanent pasture cut or cut and grazed, low N	2	2	1	1	0
Permanent pasture cut or cut and grazed, high N	2	2	1	1	1

Low N less than 250 kg/ha nitrogen per year and small clover content.
High N more than 250 kg/ha nitrogen per year or large clover content.

Phosphorus and Potassium

Soil analysis reports usually give the quantity of available phosphorus (P) and potassium (K) in terms of milligrams per litre of soil (mg/l). These amounts are also expressed as Indices (see Appendix 1). These Indices indicate the relative amounts of nutrients in the soil that are available to the crop, and range from 0 (deficient) to 9 (very large). Fertiliser recommendations are given in terms of kg/ha phosphate and potash.

Annual crop yield response to applied phosphate or potash only occurs at Indices 0 and 1 except for potatoes which respond at higher soil Indices. The amounts of fertiliser recommended for each crop at these low soil Indices are sufficient to give the economic crop response. Index 0 and 1 recommendations are always greater than offtake by the crop so that a residue is left to build up the soil reserves over a number of years.

The recommendations at Indices 2 and 3 for phosphate and Index 2 for potash are maintenance applications, except for potatoes. They are calculated to balance the amount of nutrient removed in average yielding crops, thus maintaining the soil reserves in a particular Index. Where yields are substantially different it may be appropriate to user larger or smaller amounts of fertiliser.

24

For potatoes, modest rates of phosphate and potash are recommended at higher soil phosphorus or potassium Indices because experiments show that this crop will often give an economic response to fresh fertiliser in these situations.

If soil Indices are high (Index 4 or above for phosphorus, Index 3 or above for potassium), no fertiliser is needed for most crops and the soil reserves can be allowed to decline.

Water-insoluble phosphate fertilisers

Water-insoluble phosphate fertilisers can sometimes replace water-soluble ones but many are less suitable for arable rotations.

Magnesium

As with phosphorus and potassium, soil analysis gives the quantity of available magnesium in mg/l, along with an Index (see Appendix 1). Fertiliser recommendations are expressed as kg/ha MgO.

Potatoes and sugar beet are susceptible to magnesium deficiency and show worthwhile yield responses to magnesium fertiliser when soil magnesium reserves are small. For these crops a magnesium recommendation is given under the appropriate crop heading.

Other arable crops may show visual symptoms of the deficiency on soils of low magnesium Index but seldom give a yield response to additions of magnesium. Residues from applications of magnesium to potatoes or sugar beet will satisfy the needs of other crops in the rotation.

Where sugar beet or potatoes do not feature in the rotation, magnesium fertiliser is only likely to be justified if the soil is at Index 0. In these situations apply 85 kg/ha MgO every three or four years.

Where soil magnesium reserves are small and liming is necessary, magnesian limestone should be used.

Sulphur

Inputs of sulphur from the atmosphere have fallen by 40% since 1970 and may continue to decline. A large part of England and Wales now receives less than 20 kg sulphur/ha/year from the atmosphere (see map). In these areas 50–75 kg/ha of sulphur as SO_3 is recommended in the early spring

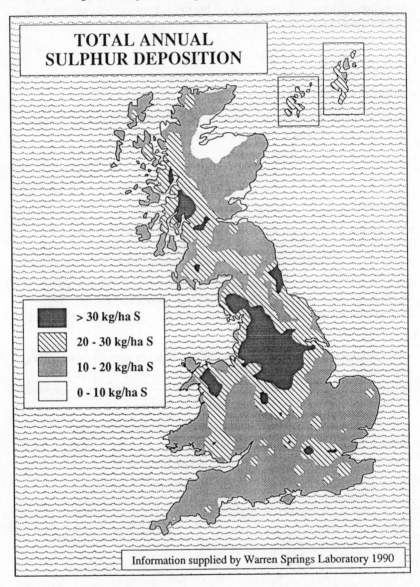

TOTAL ANNUAL
SULPHUR DEPOSITION

> 30 kg/ha S
20 - 30 kg/ha S
10 - 20 kg/ha S
0 - 10 kg/ha S

Information supplied by Warren Springs Laboratory 1990

before stem extension for oilseed rape grown on sandy soils and on shallow soils over chalk. Cereal crops may also be susceptible to sulphur deficiency and sulphur fertilisers may be needed in these areas.

A knowledge of soil type and location is currently the best guide to deficiency risk. Leaf analysis at flowering for total sulphur and nitrogen:sulphur ratio can be used to diagnose deficiency, but is not a good guide to future deficiency risk. If atmospheric deposition of sulphur declines further in the future, deficiencies and associated yield responses in oilseed rape, cereals and possibly other arable crops are likely to become more widespread, even on medium to heavy textured soils on which soil sulphur reserves are adequate for crop demand at present. Crops on fields which have received regular large inputs of organic manures in the past are less likely to show deficiency.

Sodium

Sodium fertilisers are only recommended for those crops which respond to sodium (eg sugar beet). For such crops potash can replace some but not all the sodium requirement, so that an increase should be made in the amount of potash applied when sodium is recommended but not applied.

Recommended rates of sodium application are, where appropriate, given in the recommendations for individual crops. Used at the rates indicated, sodium fertilisers should not adversely affect the physical condition of soils. Recommendations are expressed as kg/ha sodium; to convert to kg/ha salt multiply by 2.5.

Farmyard Manures and Slurries

When these materials are applied allowance should be made for the nutrients they contain and fertiliser applications reduced accordingly (see Section 2).

Trace Elements

Trace element deficiencies can occur in most arable crops, depending on soil type, soil pH and crop susceptibility. Since visual symptoms of a particular deficiency can be confused with those produced by other deficiencies, toxicities, diseases or pests, diagnosis should be verified by plant or soil analysis.

Boron (B)   Deficiency can affect sugar beet and occasionally oilseed rape on sandy soils with a pH above 6.5, particularly in dry seasons. Soil analysis prior to growing susceptible crops is a reliable means of predicting the risk of boron deficiency.

Copper (Cu)   Deficiency is not widespread but can occur mainly in cereals on sands, peats, reclaimed heathland and shallow soils over chalk. Sugar beet may also be affected. Soil analysis is useful in diagnosis but leaf copper levels do not reliably indicate copper status.

Manganese (Mn)   Deficiency occurs in many arable crops (especially sugar beet, cereals and peas) on peaty, organic and sandy soils at high pH. It also occurs less severely on many other soils when over-limed. Leaf analysis provides a reliable means of diagnosis but soil analysis is of little value.

RECOMMENDATIONS FOR ARABLE CROPS

Using the Tables

For each of the main arable crops, detailed recommendations for nitrogen (N), phosphate (P_2O_5), potash (K_2O) and magnesium (as MgO) are given in the following sections.

To find the correct recommendations for a particular crop it is important both to look in the table and to read the associated notes.

All recommendations are given in kilograms per hectare (kg/ha). The number of kilograms (kg) of the nutrient in a 50 kg bag of fertiliser is given by dividing the percentage of the nutrient by 2. For example, one 50 kg bag of a 20:10:10 NPK compound fertiliser will contain 10 kg of nitrogen, 5 kg of phosphate and 5 kg of potash.

Example

On an arable field with a soil type classified as other mineral (see Appendix 2), maincrop potatoes are to be planted after four cereal crops. The fertiliser will be broadcast.

Soil analysis has given a P Index of 2 and a K Index of 2. Using the table on page 23 the N Index is assessed as Index 0.

The table on page 40 is consulted and the recommendation for this field is found to be 220 kg/ha of nitrogen, 250 kg/ha of phosphate and 250 kg/ha of potash. (See Appendix 3 for conversion to units/acre).

28

These rates can be obtained by using straight fertilisers or by choosing a compound fertiliser to give as near the correct amounts as possible. In most cases the first priority is to get the rate of nitrogen correct. Slight variation in the rates of phosphate or potash will have less effect on yield.

CEREALS

Wheat—autumn and early winter sown

Spring nitrogen topdressing

	Index		
	0	1	2
	kg/ha		
Sandy soils	175	140	80
Shallow soils	225	190	130
Deep silty soils	180	90	0
Clays	190	110	0
Other mineral soils	210	150	70
Organic soils	120	60	0
Peaty soils	80	20	0

Timing of Applications

If total nitrogen rate is:

Less than 100 kg/haN:-
Apply as single dressing by early stem extension but not before early April

100–160 kg/haN:-
Split the dressing with 40 kg/ha mid-Feb—early-March and the remainder by early stem extension but not before early April

Over 160 kg/haN:-
Split the dressing with 40 kg/ha mid-Feb—early March and the remainder applied half at early stem extension but not before early April and the remainder at second node stage but not later than early May.

Don't forget to deduct nutrients applied as organic manures—see page 8

Breadmaking varieties

In some circumstances, application of up to 40 kg/ha in addition to that stated in the tables may be economically worthwhile to boost the content of grain protein. Application of this additional nitrogen during stem extension may give a small yield increase as well as an increase in grain protein. Application as a foliar urea spray during, but no later than, milky ripe stage can result in slightly larger increases in grain protein content but these late sprays cannot be expected to increase yield.

Yield variation

Recommendations are given for crops of average yield for the soil type. Yields of 8 t/ha are common on many soil types but will usually be nearer 7 t/ha on sandy and peaty soils. For crops with a larger or smaller yield potential the recommendation should be adjusted by plus or minus 20 kg/ha nitrogen per t/ha yield variation.

Realistic assessments of expected yield can be made for a farm by averaging yields of wheat over several years, preferably no fewer than 5 years. Yields of first and subsequent wheats should be averaged separately. Adjustment to these average levels should not be made unless individual fields consistently perform substantially worse or better than the average.

Don't forget to deduct nutrients applied as organic manures,—see page 8

Winter Barley

Spring nitrogen topdressing

	Index		
	0	1	2
Feed/Seed		kg/ha	
Sandy soils	160	120	60
Shallow soils	200	160	100
Other mineral soils	160	120	40
Organic soils	100	40	0
Peaty soils	60	0	0
Malting		kg/ha	
Sandy and shallow soils	120	80	40
Other mineral soils	110	60	40

Timing of Application

Feed/Seed

Where total nitrogen rate is less than 100 kg/ha apply as a single dressing by early stem extension, but not before late March.

Where total nitrogen rate is 100 kg/ha or greater split the dressing with 40 kg/ha mid Feb–early March and the rest by early stem extension, but not before late March.

These recommendations assume appropriate measures to control lodging by choice of variety and use of plant growth regulator. Reduce rate by 25 kg/ha if the lodging risk is high.

Malting

Where total nitrogen rate is less than 100 kg/ha apply as a single dressing by mid March.

Where total nitrogen rate is 100 kg/ha or greater split the dressing with 40 kg/ha mid Feb–early March and the rest by mid March.

Don't forget to deduct nutrients applied as organic manures—see page 8

Winter Oats, Rye and Triticale

Spring nitrogen topdressing

	Index		
	0	1	2
	kg/ha		
Sandy and shallow soils	125	100	50
Other mineral soils	110	60	30
Organic soils	70	20	0
Peaty soils	40	0	0

Timing of Application

Where total nitrogen rate is less than 100 kg/ha apply as a single dressing by early stem extension, but not before late March.

Where total nitrogen rate is 100 kg/ha or greater split the dressing with 40 kg/ha mid Feb–early March and the rest by early stem extension, but not before late March.

These recommendations assume appropriate measures to control lodging by choice of variety and use of plant growth regulator. Reduce rate by 25 kg/ha if lodging risk is high.

Don't forget to deduct nutrients applied as organic manures—see page 8

Spring Wheat

Nitrogen

	Index		
	0	1	2
		kg/ha	
Sandy and shallow soils	170	130	70
Other mineral soils	170	110	30
Organic soils	100	40	0
Peaty soils	40	0	0

Timing of Application

For crops drilled before March, apply nitrogen at early stem extension but not before early April or after early May. For amounts greater than 70 kg/ha, apply 40 kg/ha of the total in the seedbed except on sandy/shallow soils. On these soils apply 40 kg/ha at the 3 leaf stage but not before March.

For late drilled crops, all the nitrogen can be applied in the seedbed except on sandy/shallow soils where amounts greater than 70 kg/ha should be split with 40 kg/ha in the seedbed and the remainder by the 3 leaf stage.

Don't forget to deduct nutrients applied as organic manures—see page 8

Spring Barley

Nitrogen

	Index		
	0	1	2
		kg/ha	
Feed/Seed			
Sandy soils	125	90	30
Shallow soils	150	110	50
Other mineral soils	150	90	20
Organic soils	80	20	0
Peaty soils	40	0	0
Malting			
Sandy and shallow soils	100	75	20
Other mineral soils	90	50	20

Spring Oats, Rye and Triticale

Nitrogen

	Index		
	0	1	2
		kg/ha	
Sandy and shallow soils	125	90	20
Other mineral soils	100	60	30
Organic soils	70	35	0

Timing of Application

For crops drilled before March, apply nitrogen at early stem extension but not before early April or after early May. For amounts greater than 70 kg/ha, apply 40 kg/ha of the total in the seedbed except on sandy/shallow soils. On these soils apply 40 kg/ha at the 3 leaf stage but not before March.

For late drilled crops, all the nitrogen can be applied in the seedbed except on sandy/shallow soils where amounts greater than 70 kg/ha should be split with 40 kg/ha in the seedbed and the remainder by the 3 leaf stage.

Don't forget to deduct nutrients applied as organic manures—see page 8

All Cereals

Phosphate and Potash

	Index				
	0	1	2	3	Over 3
STRAW PLOUGHED IN/INCORPORATED			kg/ha		
Winter Wheat (8 t/ha)					
Phosphate	110	85	60M	60M	0
Potash	95	70	45M	0	0
Spring Wheat (6 t/ha)					
Phosphate	95	70	45M	45M	0
Potash	85	60	35M	0	0
Barley, Oats, Rye, Triticale (6 t/ha)					
Phosphate	95	70	45M	45M	0
Potash	85	60	35M	0	0
STRAW REMOVED					
Winter Wheat (8 t/ha)					
Phosphate	120	95	70M	70M	0
Potash	140	115	90M	0	0
Spring Wheat (6 t/ha)					
Phosphate	100	75	50M	60M	0
Potash	120	95	70M	0	0
Barley, Oats, Rye, Triticale (6 t/ha)					
Phosphate	100	75	50M	50M	0
Potash	135	110	85M	0	0

Timing of Application

The amounts of phosphate and potash are appropriate to the yields given. Where yields are likely to be greater or smaller phosphate and potash applications should be adjusted accordingly.

Apply phosphate and potash when convenient except at Index 0 or 1 when it should be applied in the seedbed.

Combine drilling is only likely to be advantageous at Index 0 or 1 for either phosphate or potash. To avoid reduced germination no more than 150 kg/ha nitrogen plus potash should be combined drilled on sandy soils.

Don't forget to deduct nutrients applied as organic manures—see page 8

Some clay soils can release 50 kg/ha potash annually.

M. This indicates a *maintenance* dressing intended to maintain soil reserves and prevent depletion of soil fertility rather than give a yield response.

Magnesium and sulphur

For magnesium and sulphur recommendation see pages 25–27.

Oilseed Rape and Linseed

Nitrogen

Winter Oilseed Rape	Index		
	0	1	2
		kg/ha	
Seedbed Nitrogen			
All mineral soils	30	0	0
Organic and peaty soils	0	0	0
Spring Nitrogen			
Sandy and shallow soils	160	100	40
Other mineral soils	160	100	40
Organic soils	100	50	0
Peaty soils	60	0	0

Timing of Spring Nitrogen Applications

Where nitrogen rate is less than 100 kg/ha apply the whole dressing during late Feb-early March at start of spring growth.

For amounts of 100 kg/ha or greater split the dressing with half at this time and the remainder by late March–early April.

The recommendations given are for a 3 t/ha crop. Adjust by plus or minus 30 kg/ha for each 0.5 t/ha variation from this.

Don't forget to deduct nutrients applied as organic manures—see page 8

Nitrogen

	Index		
	0	1	2
Spring Oilseed Rape		kg/ha	
All mineral soils	120	60	0
Organic and peaty soils	40	0	0
Linseed			
All mineral soils	80	40	0
Organic and peaty soils	0	0	0

Timing of Applications

Apply all the nitrogen in the seedbed except on sandy/shallow soils where the total rate is more than 80 kg/ha when the dressing should be split with 50 kg/ha in the seedbed and the remainder by early May.

Phosphate and Potash

	Index				
	0	1	2	3	Over 3
			kg/ha		
Oilseed rape and Linseed					
Phosphate	100	75	50M	50M	0
Potash	90	65	40M	0	0

Apply phosphate and potash when convenient except at Index 0 or 1 when it should be applied in the seedbed.

M—this indicates a maintenance dressing intended to maintain soil reserves and prevent depletion of soil fertility rather than give a yield response.

Magnesium and sulphur

For magnesium and sulphur recommendation see pages 25–27.

Don't forget to deduct nutrients applied as organic manures—see page 8

Peas and Beans

Nitrogen

Crop	Index		
	0	1	2
		kg/ha	
Peas	0	0	0
Field Beans	0	0	0

Phosphate, Potash and Magnesium

	Index				
	0	1	2	3	Over 4
			kg/ha		
Peas and beans					
Phosphate	75	50	30M	30M	0
Potash	120	50	30M	0	0
Magnesium	150	100	0	0	0

Timing of Applications

No nitrogen needed.

Seedbed phosphate and potash only needed at Index 0 and 1.

M—this indicates a maintenance dressing intended to maintain soil reserves and prevent depletion of soil fertility rather than to give a yield response.

Don't forget to deduct nutrients applied as organic manures—see page 8

Potatoes—Maincrop and Second Earlies

Nitrogen

	Index		
	0	1	2
		kg/ha	
Sandy and shallow soils	240	200	130
Other mineral soils	220	160	100
Organic soils	180	130	80
Peaty soils	130	90	50

Potatoes—Earlies/canning/seed

Nitrogen

Sandy and shallow soils	180	130	80
Other mineral soils	160	110	70

Phosphate, Potash and Magnesium

	Index					
	0	1	2	3	4	Over 4
			kg/ha			
Potatoes Maincrop/2nd earlies						
Phosphate	350	300	250	200	100	0
Potash	350	300	250	150	100	0
Magnesium	165	85	0	0	0	0
Potatoes earlies/canning						
Phosphate	350	300	250	200	200	0
Potash	180	150	120	60	60	0
Magnesium	165	85	0	0	0	0
Seed Potatoes						
Phosphate	350	300	250	150	100	0
Potash	350	300	250	150	100	0
Magnesium	165	85	0	0	0	0

Don't forget to deduct nutrients applied as organic manures—see page 8

Timing of Applications

Apply all nitrogen in the seedbed except on sandy/shallow soils where the crop is irrigated when the dressing should be split, half in the seed bed and half at tuber initiation.

On some late-maturing maincrop varieties nitrogen rates can be reduced if they are not grown to full maturity.

Where crops are to be harvested earlier than average, nitrogen rates can be reduced by 30 kg/ha N for first earlies, and 50 kg/ha for second earlies.

Phosphate

Potatoes are very responsive to phosphorus, but the rate of response is less at high soil Indices. The whole phosphate application should be applied in the spring and phosphate should be applied to the seedbed. Only materials containing a large proportion of water-soluble phosphate should be used for potatoes.

Potash

Maincrop recommendations are based on crops of around 40 t/ha. Yields greater than this will remove proportionally more potash. This greater removal will need to be balanced at some stage in the rotation. Where the rate of potash is more than 300 kg/ha apply half in the autumn/winter and the remainder to the seedbed. For light sandy soils, amounts greater than 300 kg/ha should be applied post-Christmas immediately after ploughing. For other situations apply the potash in the spring.

Don't forget to deduct nutrients applied as organic manures—see page 8

Sugar beet

Nitrogen

	Index		
	0	1	2
	kg/ha		
Sandy and shallow soils	125	100	75
Deep silty soils	80	50	25
Other mineral soils	100	75	50
Organic soils	75	50	25
Peaty soils	50	25	0

Timing of Applications

40 kg/ha of the total nitrogen should be applied in the seedbed or immediately post drilling and the remainder after full emergence at the 2 true leaf stage. Seedbed potash is only needed at Index 0 and phosphate at Indices 0 and 1.

Phosphate, Potash and Magnesium

	Index				
	0	1	2	3	Over 3
	kg/ha				
Phosphate	100	75	50M	50M	0
Potash	200	100	75	75	0
Magnesium	165	85M	0	0	0

M. This indicates a *maintenance* dressing intended to maintain the soil reserves and prevent depletion of soil fertility rather than to give a yield response.

Don't forget to deduct nutrients applied as organic manures—see page 8

Potash

Recommendations are based on crops of around 40 t/ha. Yields greater than this will remove proportionally more potash. This greater removal will need to be balanced at some stage in the rotation.

Where tops are carted off removal of potash is increased by about 150 kg/ha. Potash applications should be increased by this amount, either for the beet or elsewhere in the rotation, to avoid depletion of soil reserves.

Sodium

Sugar beet is responsive to sodium which is recommended for all soils except organic, peaty and Fen silt soils, which generally contain adequate sodium.

Sodium can be applied as agricultural salt at 400 kg/ha (150 kg/ha sodium).

The quantity of sodium recommended does not have any adverse effect on soil structure, even on soils of low stability.

If sodium is recommended, but not applied, increase potash by 100 kg/ha.

Don't forget to deduct nutrients applied as organic manures—see page 8

Forage Crops

Nitrogen

	Index		
	0	1	2
Crop		kg/ha	
Forage Maize[1]	60	~~40~~ *80	30
Forage Swedes and Turnips[2]	100	50	25
Forage Rape and Stubble Turnips[3]	100	75	50
Mangels, Fodder Beet and Kale	125	100	75
Forage Rye and Forage Triticale	70	20	0

*(handwritten: * eg.)*

Timing of Applications

Apply all nitrogen in seedbed for all crops.

Notes

(1) In England and Wales the response of forage maize to applied nitrogen is variable. The application of these recommendations is worthwhile even when organic manures have been applied.

Applications of organic manures should contain no more than 250 kg/ha total nitrogen as recommended in the Code of Good Agricultural Practice for the Protection of Water.

(2) An application of at least 20 kg/ha nitrogen should be made even if organic manure applied when sown after grass or forage rye from which an early season cut has been taken.

Excess nitrogen can reduce the quality of culinary swedes harvested from a dual-purpose crop. Full allowance should be made for available nitrogen when organic manures are also applied.

(3) When grown as a catch crop after cereals apply no more than 75 kg/ha nitrogen at Index 0. Further reductions may be made if the soil is moist and has been cultivated.

Don't forget to deduct nutrients applied as organic manures—see page 8

*(handwritten note at bottom: * Apparently indices for maize assume applied slurry.)*

44

Phosphate and potash

	Index				
	0	1	2	3	Over 3
Forage Maize			kg/ha		
Phosphate	80	60	40M	0	0
Potash	180	150	120M	0	0
Forage Swedes and Turnips					
Phosphate	150	100	50	50	25M
Potash	150	125	100	60	0
Stubble Turnips and Forage Rape					
Phosphate	75	50	25M	0	0
Potash	100	75	50M	50M	0
Fodder Beet and Mangels					
Phosphate	100	75	50M	50M	0
Potash[1][2][3]	200	100	75	75	0
Kale					
Phosphate	100	75	25M	0	0
Potash	100	75	50M	50M	0
Forage Rye and Forage Triticale					
Phosphate	110	60	60M	60M	0
Potash	110	60	40M	0	0

M. This indicates a *maintenance* dressing intended to maintain the soil reserves and prevent depletion of soil fertility rather than to give a yield response.

P and K need only be applied to the seedbed at Index 0 or 1.

For stubble turnips sown after mid August, apply 50 kg/ha phosphate at Index 0 only.

(1) Recommendations are based on crops of around 40 t/ha. Yields greater than this will remove proportionately more potash. This greater removal will need to be balanced at some stage in the rotation.

(2) Where tops are carted off removal of potash is increased by around 150 kg/ha. Potash applications should be increased by this amount, either for the crop or elsewhere in the rotation, to avoid depletion of soil reserves.
Salt is recommended for mangels and fodder beet on all soils except Fen silts and peats. Apply 400 kg/ha of agricultural salt (150 kg/ha sodium) well before drilling.

(3) If sodium is recommended, but not applied, increase potash by 100 kg/ha.

Magnesium

For magnesium recommendation see page 25.

Don't forget to deduct nutrients applied as organic manures—see page 8

45

Ryegrass grown for seed

Nitrogen

	Index		
	0	1	2
		kg/ha	
Sandy and shallow soils	150	110	40
Other mineral soils	130	70	20

Note

Smaller rates may be applicable in the second year or if a seed crop is harvested after a silage cut. See pages 99 and 106–109 for recommendations for grass establishment and silage.

Phosphate and Potash

	Index				
	0	1	2	3	Over 3
			kg/ha		
Phosphate	100	60	30M	30M	0
Potash	150	120	90M	0	0

Timing of Applications

Apply all nitrogen during March except when the total rate is more than 120 kg/ha when the dressing should be split with half at this time and the remainder 4 weeks later.

Phosphate and potash can be applied at any convenient time except at Index 0 when the dressing should be applied in the spring of the harvest year.

Magnesium

For magnesium recommendation see page 25.

Don't forget to deduct nutrients applied as organic manures—see page 8

Whole Crop Cereal Silage

Apply fertiliser as for a grain crop, straw removed (see pages 29–36).

Phosphate and potash need only be applied to the seedbed at Index 0 or 1.

Magnesium

For magnesium recommendation see page 25.

Don't forget to deduct nutrients applied as organic manures—see page 8

Vegetables and bulbs

SECTION 4
VEGETABLES AND BULBS

SOIL SAMPLING

The results of a soil analysis are only as good as the sample on which they are based. To give meaningful results, a soil sample must be representative of the area sampled and taken to a uniform depth (normally 15 cm). Uniformity of sampling depth is particularly important where crops are established without ploughing.

Areas of land known to differ in some important respects (eg soil type, previous cropping, applications of manure, fertiliser or lime) should be sampled separately. Small areas known to differ from the majority of a field should be excluded from the sample. A sample of 25 individual sub-samples (cores) will be adequate for a uniform area. The sub-sample points must be selected systematically, with an even distribution over the whole area. This may be achieved by following the pattern of a letter 'W' and taking sub-samples at regular intervals. When doing this, avoid headlands and the immediate vicinity of hedges and trees or other unusual features. On soils where acidity is known to occur spot testing with soil indicator over the whole area will indicate if acidity is present in patches. This can occur in areas where soils generally contain free lime.

Fields growing vegetables should be sampled for analysis every three years.

SOIL ACIDITY AND LIMING

The soil pH is a measure of acidity or alkalinity and ranges from about 4.0 (very acid), when most crops will fail, to about 8.0 for soils which are naturally rich in lime or have been over-limed.

The lime requirement of an acid soil is assessed and reported in tonnes per hectare (t/ha) of ground limestone or ground chalk. The amount of lime recommended for soils of the same pH may vary depending on soil texture and organic matter content. The value quoted on a soil analysis report is the amount of lime required to maintain a 20 cm depth of mineral soil at pH 6.5. Where soil is known to be acid to a depth greater than 20 cm a proportionately greater quantity of lime should be applied. Where dressings in excess of 12 t/ha are required, half should be deeply cultivated into the soil and then ploughed down and the remainder applied to the surface and worked in. Although recommendations are quoted in terms of ground limestone or ground chalk, other forms of lime can be used provided the rate of application is adjusted to take account of difference in neutralising value (NV).

Any lime needed should be applied well before sowing or planting. Because it can take some months for lime to correct soil acidity it is unwise to grow a crop which is sensitive to acidity immediately after liming a very acid field. However, if a crop is failing because of acidity, improvements can often be obtained by applying lime top-dressing as soon as possible.

Over-liming should be avoided, particularly on sandy and peaty soils, as it can induce deficiencies of trace elements such as manganese and boron.

PLANT NUTRIENTS

Nitrogen

The following nitrogen recommendations are based on the soil nitrogen Index. This Index system uses the expected residues from previous crops to assess the available nitrogen in the soil.

There are three soil nitrogen Indices. Fields in Index 0 have small nitrogen reserves and more nitrogen fertiliser is needed compared with fields in Index 1. Index 2 soils have the greatest soil nitrogen reserves.

Usually it is only necessary to consider the last crop grown to determine the nitrogen Index, but after lucerne, long leys and permanent pasture it is necessary to consider histories of longer than one year. Previous dressing of animal manure should also be taken into account.

Soil Mineral Nitrogen Analysis—Where residues are potentially very large (eg when animal manures have been applied) the use of Soil Mineral Nitrogen analysis can be used to determine the available nitrogen in the soil profile. (Soil sampling and analysis, page 3).

Nitrogen requirements for a second crop in the same year

When a second vegetable crop is grown in the same season the nitrogen requirements are greatly reduced because of the residual nitrogen available from the previous crop. It is difficult to estimate the quantity of available nitrogen but a simple guide is to base the nitrogen index on the previous crop grown in the same year and the amount of nitrogen (including organic nitrogen) applied to it.

Nitrogen applied to preceding vegetable crops

Nitrogen Index for second crop in same year

more than 200 kg/ha	2
100 to 200 kg/ha	1
less than 100 kg/ha	0

For a more accurate assessment use Soil Mineral Nitrogen Analysis.

Nitrogen Index based on last crop grown in the previous season

Index 0	Index 1	Index 2
Cereals Sugar beet	Potatoes Oilseed rape	Any crop, receiving large frequent dressings of FYM or slurry
Vegetables receiving less than 200 kg/ha N	Vegetables receiving more than 200 kg/ha N	Lucerne
Forage crops removed	Forage crops grazed	Long leys, grazed or cut and grazed receiving more than 250 kg/ha N or with high clover content
Set-aside (rotational)		
Leys (1–2 year) grazed or cut and grazed, low N	Leys (1–2 year) grazed or cut and grazed, high N	Any managed permanent pasture
Leys (1–2 year) cut only	Long leys, cut only	
Permanent pasture poor quality matted	Long leys, grazed or cut and grazed low N	

Low N less than 250 kg/ha nitrogen per year and small clover content.
High N more than 250 kg/ha nitrogen per year or large clover content.

Some crops such as peas and beans leave intermediate residues and should be regarded as being part way between Index 0 and Index 1.

To find the nitrogen Index of a field look up the last crop grown in the table above. If lucerne, long ley or permanent pasture has been grown during the last five years, look up the Index in the next table and use the higher of the two values.

Nitrogen Index—following lucerne,long leys and permanent pasture

	1st crop	2nd crop	3rd crop	4th crop	5th crop
Lucerne	2	2	1	0	0
Long leys cut only	1	1	0	0	0
Long leys grazed or cut and grazed, low N	1	1	0	0	0
Long leys grazed or cut and grazed, high N	2	2	1	0	0
Permanent pasture poor quality, matted	0	0	0	0	0
Permanent pasture cut only, or cut and grazed with low N	2	2	1	1	0
Permanent pasture grazed or cut and grazed with high N	2	2	1	1	1

Low N less than 250 kg/ha N per year and small clover content
High N more than 250 kg/ha N per year or large clover content

Phosphorus and potassium

Soil analysis reports usually give the quantity of available phosphorus (P) and potassium (K) in terms of milligrams per litre of soil (mg/l). These amounts are also expressed as Indices (see Appendix 1). These Indices indicate the relative amounts of nutrients in the soil that are available to the crop, and range from 0 (deficient) to 9 (very large). Fertiliser recommendations are given in terms of kg/ha phosphate and potash.

At low soil Indices the recommendations for phosphate and potash are adequate to increase yields and also to leave a residue that will build up soil reserves over a number of years. In many soils, the available phosphorus and potassium are such that yield increases from applying phosphate and potash are small. In this situation the purpose in applying phosphate and potash is to maintain soil levels. The amounts of phosphate and potash recommended are those needed to replace the nutrient removed by typical crop yields, and are referred to as maintenance dressings. Where yields are substantially different it may be appropriate to use larger or smaller amounts of fertiliser.

If soil Indices are high (Index 5 or above for phosphorus, Index 4 or above for potassium), no fertiliser is needed for most crops and the soil reserves can be allowed to decline.

Magnesium

As for phosphorus and potassium, soil analysis gives the quantity of available magnesium in mg/l, along with an Index (see Appendix 1). Fertiliser recommendations are expressed as kg/ha MgO.

At magnesium Index 0, magnesium should be applied for all vegetable crops.

Where soil magnesium status is low and liming is necessary, magnesian limestone should be used.

Sulphur

Inputs of sulphur from the atmosphere have fallen by 40% since 1970 and may continue to decline. A large part of the country now receives less than 20 kg sulphur/ha/year from the atmosphere (see map, page 26). Experiments on oilseed rape in these areas on shallow soils over chalk and on sandy soils have shown yield responses to sulphur fertiliser.

Vegetable brassicae, particularly when grown as the second crop in a season, may respond to sulphur in areas of low sulphur deposition.

A knowledge of soil type and location is the best guide to deficiency risk. Leaf analysis for total sulphur and nitrogen:sulphur ratio can be used to diagnose deficiency, but is not a definitive guide to future deficiency risk. If atmospheric deposition of sulphur declines further in the future, deficiency and associated yield response are likely to become more widespread, even on deep medium to heavy textured soils on which soil sulphur reserves are presently adequate for crop demand. Crops on fields which have received regular large inputs of organic manure in the past are less likely to show deficiency.

Sodium

Sodium fertilisers are only recommended for those crops (eg carrots and celery) which respond to sodium. A reduction can be made in the amount of potash when sodium is also applied.

Recommended rates of sodium application are given for individual crops. Used at the rates indicated, sodium fertilisers should not adversely affect the physical condition of soils. Recommendations are expressed as kg/ha Na. To convert to kg/ha NaCl (salt) multiply by 2.5.

Fertilisers

Application of fertiliser

Application of nitrogen and potash can reduce germination and damage seedling roots, especially in dry, sandy soils. To reduce this risk, fertiliser should be worked thoroughly into the soil before sowing or planting. Phosphate and potash fertilisers can be applied some weeks before sowing, but nitrogen may be lost by leaching if applied too early.

Not more than 100 kg/ha nitrogen should be applied immediately before drilling vegetables and the remainder should be applied as an early post emergence topdressing. Where heavy dressings of potash fertiliser are needed, especially in conjunction with large nitrogen dressings, part of the potassium requirement should be applied before ploughing and the remainder well worked into the seedbed.

Farmyard Manures and Slurries

When these materials are applied allowance should be made for the nutrients they contain and fertiliser applications reduced accordingly (see Section 2).

Trace elements

Trace element deficiencies can occur in many vegetable crops, depending on soil type, soil pH and crop susceptibility.

These deficiencies can usually be identified by visual diagnosis but should be checked by leaf and soil analysis.

Boron (B)   Swedes are the most susceptible crop to boron deficiency, but beetroot, carrots, celery and cauliflower can also be affected. It occurs on light sandy soils with pH values greater than 6.5. The deficiency can be confirmed by leaf and soil analysis.

Copper (Cu)   Copper deficiency is less common, but may occur on peaty soils, sands (especially reclaimed heathland or moorland) and organic soils over chalk. Onions are the most susceptible crop and carrots are also affected. Soil analysis is useful in diagnosis but leaf copper levels do not reliably indicate copper status.

Manganese (Mn)   Most crops can be affected by manganese deficiency but peas, beans, carrots, beetroot, onions and celery are most susceptible. This deficiency is common on peaty, organic and sandy soils especially if they have been over-limed. Leaf analysis provides a reliable means of diagnosis but soil analysis is of little value.

Molybdenum (Mo)   Molybdenum deficiency is always associated with soils of low pH. Cauliflowers are susceptible to this deficiency and show 'whiptail' symptoms. Deficiency can be confirmed by leaf and soil analysis.

RECOMMENDATIONS FOR VEGETABLE CROPS

Using the tables

For each of the main vegetable crops, detailed recommendations for nitrogen (N), phosphate (P_2O_5), potash (K_2O) and magnesium (as MgO) are given in the following sections.

To find the correct recommendations for a particular crop it is important both to look in the table and to read the associated notes.

All recommendations are given in kilograms per hectare (kg/ha). The number of kilograms (kg) of the nutrient in a 50 kg bag of fertiliser is given by dividing the percentage of the nutrient by 2. For example, one 50 kg bag of a 20:10:10 NPK compound fertiliser will contain 10 kg of nitrogen, 5 kg of phosphate and 5 kg of potash.

Example

On a field with a medium-textured soil, (see Appendix 2) Brussels sprouts are to be grown after a crop of potatoes.

Soil analysis has given a P Index of 2, a K Index of 1 and a Mg Index of 1. Using the table on page 53 the N Index is assessed as Index 1.

The table on page 60 is consulted and the recommendation for this field is found to be 250 kg/ha of nitrogen, 75 kg/ha of phosphate and 175 kg/ha of potash. The notes below the table on page 60 indicate that only 100 kg/ha of the total nitrogen recommendation should be applied in the seedbed. (See Appendix 3 for conversion to imperial units).

These rates can be obtained by using straight fertilisers or by choosing a compound fertiliser to give as near as possible the correct amounts. In most cases the first priority is to get the rate of nitrogen correct. Slight variation in the rates of phosphate or potash will have less effect on yield.

Asparagus

Nitrogen

	Index		
	0	1	2
	kg/ha		
Asparagus establishment[1]	150	75	50
Asparagus second year[2]	80	80	80
Asparagus subsequent years[3]	100	100	100

(1) Apply not more than 100 kg/ha at sowing or planting. The remainder should be applied when the crop is fully established, together with a further 75 kg/ha as a top dressing.

(2) Apply nitrogen by end Feb–early March.

(3) Apply up to half the nitrogen by end Feb–early March and the remainder after cutting. On sands of inherently low fertility an extra 75 kg/ha nitrogen may be needed.

Phosphate, Potash and Magnesium (kg/ha)

	Index					
	0	1	2	3	4	Over 4
	kg/ha					
Asparagus establishment						
Phosphate	175	150	125	100	75	0
Potash	250	225	200	150	125	0
Asparagus second year						
Phosphate	100	100	75	75	50	0
Potash	100	50	25	25	0	0
Asparagus subsequent years						
Phosphate	75	75	50	50	25	0
Potash	100	50	25	25	0	0
All crops						
Magnesium	150	100	0	0	0	0

Don't forget to deduct nutrients applied as organic manures—see page 8

Brussels Sprouts and Cabbages

Nitrogen

	Index		
	0	1	2
	kg/ha		
Brussels Sprouts[1]			
Deep silty soils	210	120	30
Other mineral soils	300	250	200
Cabbage Summer/Chinese/Autumn/			
Savoy-pre-xmas/Winter-pre-xmas[1],[2]	300	240	180
Cabbage White storage[1]	250	190	130
Cabbage Spring[3]	75	50	25

(1) Apply no more than 100 kg/ha at sowing or planting. The remainder should be applied when the crop is fully established.
(2) Winter and savoy crops intended for post Christmas cutting should have their early nitrogen application reduced by 100–150 kg/ha and may need a later top dressing of up to 75 kg/ha.
(3) Apply all nitrogen at sowing or planting and apply up to 250 kg/ha nitrogen as a top dressing 6 to 8 weeks before harvest. The exact rate used will depend on the season, the time of marketing and the expected yield.

Phosphate, Potash and Magnesium

	Index					
	0	1	2	3	4	Over 4
	kg/ha					
Brussels sprouts						
Phosphate	175	125	75	50	25	0
Potash	200	175	125	60	0	0
All Cabbages						
Phosphate	200	125	75	50	25	0
Potash	300	250	175	75	0	0
All crops						
Magnesium	150	100	0	0	0	0

Don't forget to deduct nutrients applied as organic manures—see page 8

60

Cauliflowers and Calabrese

Nitrogen

	Index		
	0	1	2
	kg/ha		
Cauliflower Summer/Autumn[1]	250	190	130
Cauliflower Winter hardy/Roscoff[2],[3]	75	40	0
Calabrese[1]	250	190	130

(1) Apply not more than 100 kg/ha at sowing or planting. The remainder should be applied when the crop is fully established.
(2) Apply all nitrogen in seedbed.
(3) Apply up to 200 kg/ha as a top dressing 6–8 weeks before harvest depending on the season and the expected yield. The maximum rate should only be applied to late-harvested crops of large yield potential.

Phosphate, Potash and Magnesium

	Index					
	0	1	2	3	4	Over 4
	kg/ha					
All cauliflowers						
Phosphate	175	125	75	50	25	0
Potash	300	200	125	60	0	0
Calabrese						
Phosphate	150	75	60	60	30	0
Potash	150	100	75	50	0	0
All crops						
Magnesium	150	100	0	0	0	0

Don't forget to deduct nutrients applied as organic manures—see page 8

61

Celery

Nitrogen

	Index		
	0	1	2
	kg/ha		
Celery[1]			
Mineral soils	75	75	75
Fen peats, loamy and sandy peats	0	0	0
Peaty loams	50	50	50
Moss peats[2]	100	100	100
Self-blanching			
Mineral soil and Fen peats[2]	75	75	75
Moss peats[2]	125	125	125

(1) Apply all nitrogen in seedbed.
   Apply up to 150 kg/ha nitrogen as top dressings, commencing when the plants are fully established.
(2) Apply a top dressing of 75–150 kg/ha nitrogen 4–6 weeks after planting.

Phosphate, Potash, Magnesium and Sodium

	Index					
	0	1	2	3	4	Over 4
	kg/ha					
All Celery						
Phosphate	200	150	125	100	60	0
Potash	400	350	300	200	100	0
Magnesium	150	100	0	0	0	0

Celery is responsive to sodium and salt is recommended on all soils except Fen peats and Fen silts which generally contain adequate sodium. Apply 400 kg/ha agricultural salt (150 kg/ha sodium). Unless analysis has shown low sodium levels the salt should be ploughed in or worked into the soil at least one month before planting out or drilling.

Don't forget to deduct nutrients applied as organic manures—see page 8

Peas and Beans

Nitrogen

	Index		
	0	1	2
		kg/ha	
Broad Beans[1]	60	25	0
Dwarf and Runner Beans[2]	150	100	75
Peas	0	0	0

(1) Apply all nitrogen to the seedbed if sown in spring.
(2) Apply not more than 100 kg/ha in the seedbed. The remainder should be applied when the crop is fully established. A top dressing of up to 75 kg/ha nitrogen may be applied to runner beans at early picking stage if the crop has a poor appearance.

Phosphate and Potash

	Index				
	0	1	2	3	Over 3
			kg/ha		
Broad Beans					
Phosphate	250	200	150	50	0
Potash	250	150	100	50	0
French and Runner Beans					
Phosphate	250	200	150	50	0
Potash	275	175	100	50	0
Peas					
Phosphate	75	50	25	25	0
Potash	120	50	25	0	0

Seedbed phosphate or potash is only needed at Index 0 or 1.

Don't forget to deduct nutrients applied as organic manures—see page 8

Magnesium

All peas and beans

	Index				
	0	1	2	3	Over 3
			kg/ha		
	150	100	0	0	0

Lettuce, Radish, Sweetcorn and Courgettes

Nitrogen

	Index		
	0	1	2
		kg/ha	
Lettuce summer[1]			
Sandy soils	200	160	100
Other mineral soils	180	120	60
Organic soils	150	90	30
Peaty soils	100	60	0
Radish[2]	60	25	0
Sweetcorn[2]	100	75	50
Courgettes[3]	100	75	50

(1) Apply not more than 100 kg/ha at sowing or planting. The remainder should be applied when the crop is fully established.
(2) Apply all nitrogen in seedbed.
(3) Apply in the seedbed. When the crop is fully established, a further 75 kg/ha nitrogen should be applied.

Don't forget to deduct nutrients applied as organic manures—see page 8

Phosphate, Potash and Magnesium

	Index					
	0	1	2	3	4	Over 4
				kg/ha		
Lettuce						
Phosphate	300	300	250	50	25	0
Potash	175	125	100	50	0	0
Radish						
Phosphate	100	50	25	25	25	0
Potash	275	150	100	50	0	0
Sweet Corn						
Phosphate	150	100	50	50	0	0
Potash	150	100	50	50	0	0
Courgettes						
Phosphate	200	125	60	60	30	0
Potash	250	200	125	60	0	0
All crops						
Magnesium	150	100	0	0	0	0

Where more than one crop of lettuce or radish is grown in the same season there should be sufficient residues of phosphate and potash from the first crop. Further application is not required for succeeding crops, except at Indices of 0 or 1 when half the rate recommended above should be applied.

Don't forget to deduct nutrients applied as organic manures—see page 8

65

Onions and Leeks

Nitrogen

	Index		
	0	1	2
		kg/ha	
Bulb Onions spring sown			
Mineral soils	90	60	30
Peaty soils	30	0	0
Bulb Onions autumn sown[1]			
Spring topdressing			
Mineral soils	100	70	40
Peaty soils	60	0	0
Salad Onions summer/autumn[2]	125	75	50
Salad Onions over wintered			
Spring top dressing[3]	125	75	50
Leeks[2],[4]			
Mineral soils	150	90	30
Peaty soils	60	30	0

(1) Apply up to 50 kg/ha in the seedbed at Index 0 on mineral soils.
(2) Apply not more than 100 kg/ha in the seedbed. The remainder should be applied when the crop is fully established.
(3) Apply 25 kg/ha nitrogen in the seedbed at planting.
(4) On all soils except peats a top dressing of up to 100 kg/ha nitrogen may be required depending on the appearance of the crop.

Don't forget to deduct nutrients applied as organic manures—see page 8

Phosphate, Potash and Magnesium

	Index					
	0	1	2	3	4	Over 4
				kg/ha		
Bulb Onions						
Phosphate	300	250	150	50	25	0
Potash	275	150	125	50	0	0
Salad Onions summer/autumn						
Phosphate	250	200	125	50	25	0
Potash	125	100	75	50	0	0
Salad Onions winter						
Phosphate	250	200	125	50	25	0
Potash	250	150	125	50	0	0
Leeks						
Phosphate	300	250	150	50	25	0
Potash	275	150	125	50	0	0
All crops						
Magnesium	150	100	0	0	0	0

Don't forget to deduct nutrients applied as organic manures—see page 8

Root Vegetables

Nitrogen

	Index		
	0	1	2
		kg/ha	
Beetroot[1]	250	190	130
Parsnips, Swedes & Maincrop Turnips			
Mineral soils	100	40	0
Peaty soils	60	40	0
Early Turnips[1]	160	100	40
Carrots—maincrop & early[2]			
Mineral soils	60	25	0
Peaty soils	0	0	0

(1) Apply not more than 100 kg/ha in the seedbed. The remainder should be
    applied when the crop is fully established.
(2) Apply all nitrogen in seedbed.

**Don't forget to deduct nutrients applied as organic manures—see
page 8**

Phosphate, Potash and Magnesium

	Index					
	0	1	2	3	4	Over 4
			kg/ha			
Beetroot						
Phosphate	100	100	100	50	25	0
Potash	300	200	200	100	0	0
Parsnips						
Phosphate	175	100	75	60	30	0
Potash	225	150	150	75	0	0
Swedes						
Phosphate	150	100	50	50	25	0
Potash	250	200	150	75	0	0
Turnips						
Phosphate	150	100	50	50	25	0
Potash	250	200	150	75	0	0
Carrots—maincrop						
Phosphate	250	150	125	50	25	0
Potash	250	150	125	50	0	0
Carrots—early						
Phosphate	300	250	175	100	75	0
Potash	250	150	125	50	0	0
All crops						
Magnesium	150	100	0	0	0	0

Seedbed phosphate and potash are only needed at Index 0 or 1.

Apply sodium (150 kg/ha) to carrots grown on sandy soils. When sodium is used reduce the potash recommendation by 60 kg/ha. Sodium should be worked deeply into the soil before drilling or be ploughed in.

Don't forget to deduct nutrients applied as organic manures—see page 8

Bulbs and Bulb Flowers

Nitrogen

	Index		
	0	1	2
		kg/ha	
Bulbs	100	40	0

Phosphate, Potash and Magnesium

	Index				
	0	1	2	3	Over 3
			kg/ha		
Bulbs					
Phosphate	125	100	75	50	0
Potash	250	200	150	100	0
Magnesium	150	100	0	0	0

Apply nitrogen as a top dressing just before crop emergence.

A top dressing of 50 kg/ha nitrogen may be required in the second year of a narcissus crop if the growth was poor in the first year.

Don't forget to deduct nutrients applied as organic manures—see page 8

Fruit and hops

SECTION 5
FRUIT AND HOPS

SOIL SAMPLING

Method of sampling

Soil samples may be taken with an auger or corer. The sample for analysis should consist of 25 cores which should be representative of the area sampled. Areas to be sampled should have had the same management for a number of years and be uniform. Areas of differing soil type should be sampled separately.

Sampling before planting

Fields intended for planting with fruit or hops should be sampled to two depths, 0 to 15 cm and 15 to 30 cm. This is particularly important on land previously in fruit, hops or grass where a depth gradient in nutrient content and acidity will probably have developed. The 15 to 30 cm sampling is not essential on land previously ploughed regularly to 25 cm or more. Sampling should be carried out before ploughing so that if lime or fertiliser needs to be ploughed down, it can be applied first. In old herbicide-strip orchards, separate samples should be taken from the grass alley and the strip, especially where lime and fertiliser have been previously applied to the strip only.

When sampling fields on non-calcareous soils where there is a risk of acidity, each core should be tested for pH in the field using soil indicator. Soil analysis of bulked samples will not necessarily show acid patches within the field.

Sampling established crops

For all established fruit and hops, sampling depth should be to 15 cm. Where soil has been undisturbed for a number of years, sampling depth must be as accurate as possible, and must include the top 5 cm layer. A tubular corer is best for this purpose.

Orchards in overall grass or overall herbicide management should be sampled within the spread of the tree branches. In orchards with herbicide strip management sampling should be restricted to the strip, excluding the grass area. Samples from soft fruit plantations and hops should be taken at random from within the area of rooting. When sampling on potentially acid soils, each core should be tested for pH in the field using soil indicator. On bare soils under herbicide management the top 5 cm should be tested with soil indicator, as acidity develops from the surface downwards. Assessment of this layer will give an early warning of liming need.

SOIL ACIDITY AND LIMING

Most fruit crops are tolerant of slight acidity and grow best around pH 6.0 to 6.5. Soil pH levels below about 5.5 can give rise to manganese toxicity, causing measley bark in apples and purple veining in some strawberry varieties. Blackcurrants are more susceptible to soil acidity and the pH should be maintained at 6.5.

Mature hops can tolerate a considerable degree of soil acidity but some varieties may suffer from manganese toxicity if excessive acidity builds up. Young hop plants are more sensitive to acidity.

It is important that soils used for fruit and hops are not overlimed as this may lead to trace element deficiencies.

Liming before planting

Any lime required should be applied and incorporated before planting. Because acidity problems occur in patches and acidity can develop rapidly under herbicide management, the whole plough layer should be limed to maintain a pH value of 6.5 in the early years of fruit or hops. Because it will be impossible to correct any acidity at depth by later lime incorporation, the quantity of lime applied before planting should be sufficient to correct the pH values of the top 40 cm of soil. Although the samples are taken to 30 cm depth laboratory calculation should account for the need to correct pH to 40 cm.

Where there is a lime requirement for the lower horizon this should be ploughed down. When only a 0 to 15 cm sample has been taken the lime requirement should be doubled and half deeply cultivated into the soil and then ploughed down. If the total requirement is less than 7.5 t/ha it should be applied after ploughing and cultivated in.

If testing with indicator shows pH levels of less than 5.0 below plough depth, seek further advice before liming or planting.

Liming established crops

Under herbicide strip management, the strip will generally become acid more quickly than the grass alley and may require more frequent liming than the alley.

The correction of acidity in undisturbed soil is slow, so it is important to check soil pH regularly and apply lime when necessary before a severe problem builds up.

Liming materials

Acid soils deficient in magnesium, should receive their lime requirement as magnesian limestone, particularly before planting. One tonne of magnesian limestone contains about 185 kg of MgO. Where soil magnesium levels are satisfactory ground chalk or limestone should be used. It is inadvisable to use coarse grades of limestone or chalk.

PLANT NUTRIENTS

Nitrogen

The following nitrogen recommendations are not based on soil analysis but on the requirement of the crop to be grown, making allowances for residues from the previous cropping. A soil nitrogen Index based on these criteria is used to assess the available nitrogen in the soil.

There are three soil nitrogen Indices. Fields in Index 0 have small nitrogen reserves and more nitrogen fertiliser is needed compared with fields in Index 1. Index 2 soils have the greatest soil nitrogen reserves.

Usually it is only necessary to consider the last crop grown to determine the nitrogen Index. But after lucerne, long leys and permanent pasture it is necessary to consider histories longer than one year. Previous dressings of animal manure should also be taken into account.

Where residues are potentially very large (eg when animal manures have been applied) the use of Soil Mineral Nitrogen analysis can be very helpful in determining the available nitrogen in the soil profile. ('Soil sampling and analysis', page 3).

For fruit plantations the nitrogen Index is most relevant in the first three years after planting when the soil nitrogen supply will be influenced by previous cropping. After establishment previous cropping has little effect on soil nitrogen supply and the nitrogen Index 0 recommendation should be used. For top fruit, nitrogen recommendations depend upon the soil management system.

Nitrogen Index based on last crop grown

Index 0	Index 1	Index 2
Cereals Sugar beet	Potatoes Oilseed rape	Any crop receiving large frequent dressings of FYM or slurry
Vegetables receiving less than 200 kg/ha N	Vegetables receiving more than 200 kg/ha N	Lucerne
Forage crops removed	Forage crops grazed	Long leys, grazed or cut and grazed receiving more than 250 kg/ha N or with high clover content
Set-aside (rotational)		
Leys (1–2 year) grazed or cut and grazed, low N	Leys (1–2 year) grazed or cut and grazed, high N	Any managed permanent pasture
Leys (1–2 year) cut only	Long leys, cut only	
Permanent pasture poor quality matted	Long leys, grazed or cut and grazed low N	

Low N less than 250 kg/ha nitrogen per year and small clover content.
High N more than 250 kg/ha nitrogen per year or large clover content.

Some crops such as peas and beans leave intermediate residues and should be regarded as being part way between Index 0 and Index 1.

To find the nitrogen Index of a field look up the last crop grown in the table above. If lucerne, long ley or permanent pasture has been grown during the last five years, look up the Index in the next table and use the higher of the two values.

Nitrogen Index—following lucerne, long leys and permanent pasture

	1st crop	2nd crop	3rd crop	4th crop	5th crop
Lucerne	2	2	1	0	0
Long leys cut only	1	1	0	0	0
Long leys grazed or cut and grazed, low N	1	1	0	0	0
Long leys grazed or cut and grazed, high N	2	2	1	0	0
Permanent pasture poor quality, matted	0	0	0	0	0
Permanent pasture cut only, or grazed or cut and grazed with low N	2	2	1	1	0
Permanent pasture grazed or cut and grazed with high N	2	2	1	1	1

Low N less than 250 kg/ha nitrogen per year and small clover content.
High N more than 250 kg/ha nitrogen per year or large clover content.

Where excess nitrogen is given, tree and bush fruits are liable to grow vegetatively with large dark green leaves. Apple quality, especially taste, firmness and storage qualities, may be adversely affected. Increasing nitrogen reduces the amount of red colour and intensifies the green colour of apples. This effect is detrimental to crop appearance and value in red coloured varieties but can be beneficial in culinary varieties such as Bramley.

Nitrogen manuring can reduce the alpha-acid content of hop cones, although up to a certain point it will produce more alpha-acid per hectare because the crop itself is greater. Where progressive Verticillium wilt is present, high rates of nitrogen will make hops more susceptible to attack from this disease. On farms where there is a risk of wilt it will be necessary to reduce applications to below those normally recommended for maximum yield.

Phosphorus

Soil analysis reports usually give the quantity of available phosphorus (P) in terms of milligrams per litre of soil (mg/l). These amounts are also expressed as Indices (see Appendix 1). These Indices indicate the relative amounts of nutrients in the soil that are available to the crop, and range from 0 (deficient) to 9 (very large).

Fertiliser rates to maintain soil phosphorus levels under established fruit crops are given at Index 2 and 3. At Index 0 and 1 larger fertiliser rates are recommended. These will be adequate to supply the crops needs and to leave a residue to build up soil reserves. If the soil Index is above 4, no fertiliser is needed for most crops and the soil reserves can be allowed to decline. Fertiliser recommendations are expressed as kg/ha phosphate.

Only materials containing predominantly water-soluble phosphate should be used.

Potassium and Magnesium

As with phosphorus, soil analysis reports give the quantity of available soil potassium(K) and magnesium(Mg) in terms of milligrams per litre of soil (mg/l).

Fertiliser rates to maintain soil potassium and magnesium reserves under established fruit crops are given at Index 2. At lower Indices greater fertiliser rates are recommended to obtain a crop response and to leave a residue that will build up soil reserves. There is a nil fertiliser recommendation above Index 2. Fertiliser recommendations are expressed as kg/ha potash. Magnesium recommendations are given in terms of kg/ha MgO.

Excessive applications of potash can affect the amount of calcium taken up by apples and this in turn may affect the storage properties of the fruit. Soil potassium should not be built up above Index 2.

To avoid induced magnesium deficiency, the soil K:Mg ratio (calculated from values of mg/l K and Mg as determined by soil analysis) should not be greater than 3:1.

All forms of potash fertiliser are water soluble. Muriate of potash can be used for most crops, but sulphate of potash should be used for raspberries, redcurrants and gooseberries where more than 120 kg/ha potash is to be applied, particularly in the spring.

Magnesium can often be supplied cheaply by using magnesian limestone, when the soil needs liming. When liming is not required, kieserite (27 per cent MgO) or calcined magnesite (80 per cent MgO) should be used. Where magnesium deficiency has been diagnosed, foliar sprays of agricultural magnesium sulphate (Epsom salts) may give more rapid control than soil dressings of magnesium fertilisers.

Farmyard manures and Slurries

When these materials are applied allowance should be made for the nutrients they contain and fertiliser applications reduced accordingly (see Section 2).

Shoddy Where medium or high grade shoddy (10–12 per cent N) has been applied regularly, the total nitrogen application (shoddy plus fertiliser nitrogen) should be adjusted, assuming two-thirds of the nitrogen content of the shoddy to be available in the year of application.

Trace Elements

Trace element deficiencies may occur in fruit crops and in hops in some areas, especially where soil pH is greater than 7. These deficiencies can often be identified by visual diagnosis but should be checked by leaf and soil analysis. Iron deficiency cannot be confirmed by analysis.

Boron (B) Boron deficiency in fruit crops is rare. There is some recent evidence suggesting a possible association between boron deficiency and some forms of apple fruit cracking. Where confirmed the deficiency can be corrected by foliar application of boron.

Copper (Cu) Copper deficiency in pears has been diagnosed on occasions particularly in orchards on sandy soils. It can be corrected by applying a foliar spray of copper.

Iron (Fe) Iron deficiency occurs commonly on fruit crops grown on shallow, calcareous soils. Either soil or foliar application of iron chelate can be used for treatment.

Manganese (Mn) Manganese deficiency can occur in fruit crops grown on slowly drained calcareous soils. It is best controlled by foliar application of manganese.

Zinc (Zn) Zinc deficiency has very occasionally been found to reduce growth and cropping of apple trees on sandy soils. This can be corrected by foliar application of zinc.

RECOMMENDATIONS FOR FRUIT

Using the tables

Recommendations for nitrogen (N), phosphate(P_2O_5), potash(K_2O) and magnesium(MgO) for fruit crops and vines are given in the following sections for a range of nutrient Indices. To find the correct recommendation for a particular crop it is important to read the introductory section for that crop. It is also necessary to take account of any footnotes to the table that are relevant to a particular recommendation.

Recommendations are given in kilograms per hectare (kg/ha) of nutrient and a metric conversion table is given in Appendix 3.

All the plant nutrients can be applied as straight fertilisers (that is, fertilisers containing one nutrient only), as compound fertilisers (containing two or more nutrients) or as organic manures. The number of kilograms (kg) of the nutrient in a 50 kg bag of fertiliser is given by dividing the percentage of the nutrient by 2. Thus a 50 kg bag of a 20:10:10 NPK compound fertiliser will contain 10 kg of nitrogen, 5 kg of phosphate and 5 kg of potash.

Example

Where dessert apples are growing with a herbicide strip system in a deep silty soil of P Index 1, K Index 2 and Mg Index 1 (from the soil analysis report), the recommendations from page 83 are:

Nitrogen	- 30 kg/ha
Phosphate	- 40 kg/ha
Potash	- 80 kg/ha
Magnesium	- 65 kg/ha

FRUIT, VINES AND HOPS BEFORE PLANTING

Where soil analysis before planting shows insufficient nutrients, it is important to correct it by thorough incorporation of appropriate amounts of lime and fertilisers. After planting the downward movement of all nutrients, except nitrogen, from the soil surface is slow. This applies particularly for phosphorus and to a lesser extent for potassium and magnesium. The recommended rates of nutrients given for a 15 cm depth of soil should be applied in the autumn before planting. Where previously ploughed land has been sampled to 15 cm depth only the recommended rates should be thoroughly incorporated before planting. Before planting top fruit, vines or hops, if the analysis shows a field to be Index 0 or 1 for phosphorus, potassium or magnesium, the appropriate nutrient rates should be ploughed down and in addition the same rate applied and thoroughly incorporated before planting.

If plough depth is less than 20 cm, the rate ploughed down should be halved.

80

Where samples have been taken from 0 to 15 cm depth and 15 to 30 cm, the appropriate nutrient rates should be ploughed down before top fruit, vines or hops are planted if the 15 to 30 cm sample is Index 0 or 1 for phosphorus, potassium or magnesium. After ploughing, the rate based on the 0 to 15 cm sample, should be applied and thoroughly incorporated before planting. If plough depth is less than 20 cm the rate ploughed down should be halved.

Where it is not possible to plough fertiliser down, the application should be limited to the amount recommended for one sampling depth only.

It is not necessary to plough fertiliser down before planting soft fruit.

Nitrogen is not required before planting.

Fruit, Vines and Hops—before planting

Nitrogen, Phosphate, Potash and Magnesium

Crop	Index					
	0	1	2	3	4	Over 4
			kg/ha			
Fruit and Vines						
Nitrogen	0	0	0	–	–	–
Phosphate	200	100	50	50	0	0
Potash	200(1)	100	50	0	0	0
Magnesium	165	125	85	0	0	0
Hops						
Nitrogen	0	0	0	–	–	–
Phosphate	250	175	125	100	50	0
Potash	300(1)	250(1)	200	150	100	0
Magnesium	250	165	85	0	0	0

(1) These rates should be applied in the autumn and well incorporated to avoid root scorch to the newly planted crop.

Don't forget to deduct nutrients applied as organic manures—see page 8

TOP FRUIT—ESTABLISHED ORCHARDS

The nitrogen recommendations given below are based on soil management system and soil type. The recommendations are intended as a guide and should be varied according to variety, rootstock, vigour, leaf or fruit analysis and appearance of foliage. The width of the herbicide strip and the

81

effectiveness of the herbicide programme can also influence nitrogen requirements. Guidance on the use of leaf analysis to modify nitrogen recommendations is given on page 87.

When nitrogen is deficient, the leaves of fruit crops tend to be small and pale green, the bark of fruit trees may be reddish in colour and shoot growth restricted. Yields are reduced due to the decrease in the number and size of fruit, which may also be highly coloured.

In grass alley/herbicide strip orchards the tree roots are largely confined to the strip and fertiliser should be applied to the herbicide strip only. Therefore the rate per treated area should remain the same but the overall fertiliser use is reduced.

For the first three years, phosphate, potash and magnesium fertilisers are not required by young trees grown in herbicide strips, providing that deficiencies of these nutrients are corrected before planting by thorough incorporation of fertiliser.

Fertigation of young trees

The addition of nutrients to the irrigation water (fertigation) can improve the growth and early cropping of young apple trees planted on sites previously cropped with apples. A benefit is more likely where the soil organic matter level and nitrogen reserves have been depleted by long term use of overall herbicide treatment to maintain a bare soil surface. Experiments indicate that the rate of nitrogen addition should be about 10 g nitrogen per tree in the first growing year increasing to 15–20 g per tree in the second and third years.

Care should be taken to ensure soils are not completely wetted to minimise the risk of nitrate leaching.

Biennial Fertiliser Application

For established crops the timing of phosphate, potash and magnesium application is not critical. If the nutrient Index is 2 or over the nutrients may be applied at twice the recommended rate every second year.

Top Fruit—established orchards

Nitrogen

Crop	Cultivated or overall herbicide	Grass/ Herbicide strip	Overall grass
		kg/ha	
Dessert apples			
Sandy and shallow soils	60	80	120
Deep silty soils	0	30	70
Clays	20	40	80
Other mineral soils	40	60	100
Culinary and cider apples			
Sandy and shallow soils	90	110	150
Deep silty soils	40	60	100
Clays	50	70	110
Other mineral Soils	70	90	130
Pears, Cherries and Plums			
Sandy and shallow soils	120	140	180
Deep silty soils	70	90	130
Clays	80	100	140
Other mineral Soils	100	120	160

Refer to page 87 for guidelines on modifying nitrogen rate according to leaf analysis.

Phosphate, Potash and Magnesium

	Index				
	0	1	2	3	Over 3
			kg/ha		
All top fruit annually					
Phosphate	80	40	20	20	0
Potash	220	150	80	0	0
Magnesium	100	65	50	0	0

Don't forget to deduct nutrients applied as organic manures—see page 8

83

SOFT FRUIT AND VINES—ESTABLISHED PLANTATIONS

For bush and cane fruits nitrogen rates may need to be modified depending on the amount of annual growth required for a particular production system. When nitrogen is deficient, leaves tend to be small and pale green.

For crops which are establishing prior to reaching full crop potential smaller rates of nitrogen are usually adequate. The rate should be adjusted according to the amount of growth required.

For established crops the timing of phosphate, potash and magnesium applications is not critical.

Soft Fruit

Nitrogen

	kg/ha
Blackcurrants	
Sandy and shallow soils	160
Deep silty soils	110
Clays	120
Other mineral Soils	140
Redcurrants, Gooseberries, Raspberries, Loganberries, Tayberries, Blackberries	
Sandy and shallow soils	120
Deep silty soils	70
Clays	80
Other mineral Soils	100
Vines	
Sandy and shallow soils	60
Deep silty soils	0
Clays	20
Other mineral Soils	40

Don't forget to deduct nutrients applied as organic manures—see page 8

Established Soft Fruit

Phosphate, Potash and Magnesium

	Index				
	0	1	2	3	Over 3
	kg/ha				
Blackcurrants, Redcurrants, Gooseberries, Raspberries, Loganberries, Tayberries					
Phosphate	110	70	40	40	0
Potash	250[1]	180[1]	120	60	0
Blackberries, Vines					
Phosphate	110	70	40	40	0
Potash	220	150	80	0	0
All Crops					
Magnesium	100	65	50	0	0

(1) Sulphate of potash should be used for raspberries, redcurrants and gooseberries when more than 120 kg/ha potash is applied.

Don't forget to deduct nutrients applied as organic manures—see page 8

Strawberries

Nitrogen

	Index		
	0	1	2
	kg/ha		
Strawberries—main season (June bearer varieties)[1],[2]			
Sandy and shallow soils	60	20	0
Deep silty soils	0	0	0
Other mineral soils	40	0	0
Strawberries—long season (ever-bearer varieties)[3],[4]			
Sandy and shallow soils	80	40	0
Deep silty soils	20	0	0
Other mineral soils	60	20	0

(1) Where total nitrogen rate is less than 40 kg/ha N apply as a single dressing after the first full harvest. Where total nitrogen rate is greater than 40 kg/ha N apply 40 kg/ha after harvest and the remainder at the start of growth in April.
(2) For spring planted crops grown intensively and cropped in their first year apply as a single dressing to the planting bed before planting.
(3) For new plantings apply in a single dressing to the planting bed.
(4) For established crops apply in a single dressing in April.

Phosphate, Potash and Magnesium

	Index				
	0	1	2	3	Over 3
			kg/ha		
Phosphate	110	70	40	40	0
Potash	220	150	80	0	0
Magnesium	100	65	50	0	0

Fertigation

Where strawberries are grown under a polythene mulch with subirrigation, nutrients can be applied in the irrigation system (Fertigation). The rate of nitrogen used should be the same as recommended for soil applied fertiliser. At Index 2 or above, maintenance rates of phosphate and potash can be applied by fertigation. However where soil phosphorus, potassium or magnesium levels are low (Indices 0 or 1) the normal recommended amount of fertiliser should be applied and cultivated into the planting bed before the soil is mulched.

LEAF ANALYSIS FOR TOP AND SOFT FRUIT

Leaf analysis is a very useful technique for the diagnosis of nutritional disorders. Separate samples should be taken in a similar manner from both good and poor areas of growth so that the results can be compared.

In addition the specification of satisfactory ranges of leaf nutrient concentration for optimum growth and cropping has proved a useful method of assessing the nutritional status of crops. Satisfactory nutrient levels are given on page 88. Where results are to be compared to the standards it is essential that a representative sample is taken at the correct time.

Because there are seasonal and other factors which influence leaf nutrient levels, leaf analysis must be interpreted with caution. Leaf nutrient levels can also vary between varieties. Where there is sufficient information the standard ranges take account of varietal differences.

Leaf analysis can be used to provide a more complete guide to the adequacy of the orchard fertiliser programme than can be obtained from soil analysis alone. Where leaf nutrient levels are below the satisfactory range an increase in fertiliser use can be considered. However, before making a change the cause should be further investigated to ensure that other factors such as soil compaction or disease are not involved.

Where the leaf nutrient level is consistently above the satisfactory range for several years there may be justification for a reduction in fertiliser use. In particular, high levels of nitrogen and potassium can have adverse effects on apple storage quality and application rates can often be reduced to advantage.

A high manganese level indicates a need to check soil pH but can also result from use of foliar feeds or fungicides containing manganese.

Leaf analysis—satisfactory nutrient ranges (% dry matter)

Crop	Leaf sampling position (a)	Nitrogen (N)	Phos-phorus (P)	Potassium (K)	Magnesium (Mg)
Apple					
Cox	1	2.6–2.8	0.20–0.25	1.2–1.6	0.20–0.25
Bramley	1	2.4–2.8	0.18–0.23	1.2–1.6	0.20–0.30
Cherries	1	2.4–2.8	0.20–0.25	1.5–2.0	0.20–0.25
Pears					
Comice	1	1.8–2.1	0.15–0.20	1.2–1.6	0.20–0.25
Conference	1	2.1–2.6	0.15–0.20	1.2–1.6	0.20–0.25
Plums	1	2.0–2.6	0.15–0.20	1.5–2.0	0.20–0.25
Blackcurrants	2	2.8–3.0	0.25–0.35	1.5–2.0	0.15–0.25
Raspberries	3	2.4–2.8	0.20–0.25	1.5–2.0	0.30–0.35
Strawberries	4	2.6–3.0	0.25–0.30	1.5–2.0	0.15–0.20
Vines	5	2.6–3.0	0.25–0.30	1.2–1.6	0.20–0.30

(a) Leaf sampling position:
1. Mid-third extension growth, sampled mid-August
2. Fully expanded leaves extension growth, sampled prior to harvest
3. Fully expanded leaves non-fruiting canes, sampled at fruit ripening
4. Lamina of recently matured leaves, sampled at fruiting stage
5. Leaf opposite basal fruit cluster at full bloom

APPLE FRUIT ANALYSIS

Analysis of fruit sampled within three weeks of picking has provided a useful indicator of the risk of some physiological disorders in stored apples. Results can also be used to rank orchards for potential storage quality.

If fruit analysis produces consistently large or small concentrations of a particular nutrient over two to three years, modification of fertiliser application should be considered. The most likely change will be a reduction in nitrogen or potash use. Fruit analysis may also show deficiencies of calcium or phosphorus which can reduce fruit storage quality. These deficiencies can be corrected by foliar sprays of calcium and phosphorus or by post-harvest treatments.

HOPS—ESTABLISHED

Fertiliser is not required in the first year after establishment of hops provided appropriate pre-planting fertilisers have been applied.

Hops require the maintenance of large soil nutrient reserves. Phosphorus levels should be maintained at Index 4, potassium at Index 3 and magnesium at Index 2. Potassium is important and care must be taken to ensure that the recommended rates are applied.

Nitrogen

The nitrogen recommendations should be split into at least two applications, the first dressing being given in late March or April and the second during May. There is some evidence that late hop varieties respond to a three timing split, with the last application no later than mid-June. The total rate should be adjusted according to variety, irrigation and soil type. It is important to apply less nitrogen where Verticillium wilt is present but the rate should not normally be reduced below 125 kg/ha nitrogen.

Established Hops

Nitrogen

	kg/ha
Deep silty soils	180
Clays	200
Other mineral soils	220

Where large and frequent applications of organic manures have been used in previous years reduce the above applications by 70 kg/ha.

Where organic manures have been applied in the previous 12 months the nitrogen rate should be reduced according to the guidelines on Page 8.

Where soil nitrogen residues are potentially very large (eg where organic manures have been used regularly) the use of Soil Mineral Nitrogen analysis can be very helpful in determining the available nitrogen in the soil profile.

Phosphate, Potash and Magnesium

	Index					
	0	1	2	3	4	Over 4
				kg/ha		
Phosphate	250	200	150	100	50	0
Potash	425	350	275	200	100	0
Magnesium	165	85	50	0	0	0

Farmyard Manure

Farmyard manure has been a traditional manure used on hops. As well as supplying nutrients it helps to improve the structure of cultivated soils. Now that few soils are cultivated there is less need for regular applications of bulky organic manures. Farmyard manure is recommended where the soil continues to be cultivated and where land is being prepared for planting.

Extreme caution should be exercised in the use of farmyard manure or slurry where Verticillium wilt is known or suspected to be present. Heavy applications of manure, in addition to supplying excess nitrogen, can reduce the soil temperature during the critical spring period. Low soil temperatures in the spring are known to make hops more susceptible to the disease.

Don't forget to deduct nutrients applied as organic manures—see page 8

Grass

SECTION 6
GRASS

SOIL SAMPLING

The results of a soil analysis are only as good as the sample on which they are based. To give meaningful results, a soil sample must be representative of the area sampled and taken to a uniform depth (7.5 cm for established grassland, 15 cm if grassland is to be ploughed out). Uniformity of sampling depth and inclusion of the grass mat are particularly important for grassland.

Areas of land known to differ in some important respects (eg soil type, previous cropping, applications of manure, fertiliser or lime) should be sampled separately. Small areas known to differ from the majority of a field should be excluded from the sample. A sample of 25 individual sub-samples (cores) will be adequate for a uniform area. The sub-sample points must be selected systematically, with an even distribution over the whole area. This may be achieved by following the pattern of a letter 'W' and taking sub-samples at regular intervals. When doing this, avoid headlands and the immediate vicinity of hedges and trees, gateways, feeding areas or other unusual features. On soils where acidity is known to occur spot testing with soil indicator over the whole area will indicate if acidity is present in patches.

Pot corers are most suitable for taking soil samples in grassland. Screw augers should not be used.

Under most grassland systems, soil nutrient levels other than inorganic nitrogen change slowly so it is not necessary to resample and analyse every year. In general, sampling every fourth year is satisfactory as a basis for fertiliser recommendations, but pH may need more frequent monitoring.

SOIL ACIDITY AND LIMING

The soil pH is a measure of acidity or alkalinity and ranges from about 4.0 (very acid), to about 8.0 for soils which are naturally rich in lime or have been over-limed.

Many grass species can tolerate more acid soil conditions than most arable crops. Grass/clover swards are less tolerant of acid soil conditions than all-grass swards, and clover is likely to become less persistent at soil pH levels below the optimum.

The optimum pH levels for continuous grass or grass clover swards are lower for peaty soils than for mineral soils.

pH 6.0—mineral soils

pH 5.3—peaty soils

In a mixed grass/arable rotation it is necessary to maintain the soil at a pH suitable for the rotation. Where the occasional cereal crop is grown in a predominantly grassland rotation, the soil pH should be maintained at pH 6.0, or 6.2 if barley is grown.

The lime requirement of an acid soil is assessed and reported in tonnes per hectare (t/ha) of ground limestone or ground chalk. The amount of lime recommended for soils of the same pH may vary depending on soil texture and organic matter content. The value quoted on a soil analysis report for grassland is the amount of lime required to maintain a 15 cm depth of mineral soil at pH 6.0. Special recommendations (eg where land is being reclaimed for agricultural use) may be made on the analysis report. Although recommendations are quoted in terms of ground limestone or ground chalk, other forms of lime can be used provided the rate of application is adjusted to take account of any difference in neutralising value (NV).

Any lime needed should be applied well before critical soil pH levels are reached since it can take some months for lime to correct soil acidity.

Over-liming should be avoided as it can induce deficiencies of trace elements such as copper, cobalt and selenium which can adversely affect livestock growth.

PLANT NUTRIENTS

Nitrogen

The following nitrogen recommendations are not based on soil analysis but on the requirement of the crop to be grown, making allowances for soil nitrogen residues from the previous cropping, grass management and manuring. The soil nitrogen supply is based on these criteria and is used to assess the nitrogen available from the soil for grass growth.

Three levels of soil nitrogen supply are recognised for these recommendations. Fields with a low level of nitrogen supply need more nitrogen compared with fields with a moderate or high nitrogen supply.

Usually it is only necessary to consider the grass management history in the last 1–3 years to determine the soil nitrogen supply, but longer histories can be relevant. Previous dressings of animal manures must also be taken into account. (See Table 9)

Nitrogen recommendations are given for predominantly ryegrass swards and intensive cutting and grazing systems as usually practised for dairy farming. Lesser rates of nitrogen will be appropriate in beef or sheep systems of lower intensity where it will not be possible to utilise the full potential of grass growth. Where growth is restricted by drought, dressings should be reduced or omitted altogether if the drought is prolonged or severe. Lesser rates of nitrogen should also be used where there will be difficulty in using all the grass produced eg on some heavy soils in high rainfall areas.

Table 9   Nitrogen available from soil for grass growth according to previous management

(a) Ley-arable rotations:
New reseeds: after 2 or more years arable:

Last crop cereal or sugar beet	Low
Last crop potatoes, rape, peas or beans	Moderate

Other grass (including reseeds after 1 year arable):

Nitrogen inputs less than 100 kg/ha N, no clover	Low
Nitrogen inputs 100–250 kg/ha N or good clover content	Moderate
Nitrogen input more than 250 kg/ha N	High

(b) Continuous grass systems:
New reseeds (grass reseeds following grass):

Nitrogen inputs less than 100 kg/ha N, no clover	Low
Nitrogen inputs more than 100 kg/ha N or sward with large clover content	High

Established grass:

Nitrogen inputs less than 100 kg/ha N, no clover	Low
Nitrogen inputs 100–250 kg/ha N or good clover content	Moderate
Nitrogen inputs more than 250 kg/ha N	High

Notes:

Nitrogen input figures refer to use on previous grass and include **manure** nitrogen.
For swards which were **cut only**, reduce N supply by one category.
If heavy, frequent applications of manure have been made, the nitrogen supply will be **high**.

Phosphorus and potassium

Soil analysis reports give the quantity of available phosphorus (P) and potassium (K) in terms of milligrams per litre of soil (mg/l). These amounts are also expressed as Indices (see Appendix 1). These Indices indicate the relative amounts of nutrients in the soil that are available to the crop, and range from 0 (deficient) to 9 (very high). Fertiliser recommendations are given in terms of kg/ha of phosphate (P_2O_5) and potash (K_2O).

In the absence of soil analysis the application rates appropriate to P Index 2 and K Index 2 can be taken as a rough guide for grazed grass, and P Index 2, K Index 1 for conserved grass. It is not advisable to use these rates for many years without checking the nutrient status of the soil by analysis.

A yield response by grass to applied phosphorus or potassium usually only occurs at Indices 0 and 1. The quantity of fertiliser recommended at these low soil Indices is sufficient to give the economic crop response and to build up the soil nutrient reserves. Grass/clover swards are more sensitive to low phosphorus and potassium than grass-only swards.

The recommendations at Indices 2 and 3 for phosphate and Index 2 for potash are maintenance applications. These are calculated to balance the amount of nutrient removed in average crops, thus maintaining the soil reserves. Where yields are substantially different it may be appropriate to use larger or smaller amounts of fertiliser.

If soil Indices are high (Index 4 or above), no fertiliser is needed for most crops and the soil reserves can be allowed to decline.

Water-insoluble phosphate fertilisers

Water-insoluble phosphate fertilisers can sometimes be used to replace water-soluble ones but may be less suitable for rotations which include arable crops.

Magnesium

As with phosphorus and potassium, soil analysis gives the quantity of available magnesium in mg/l, along with an Index (see Appendix 1). Fertiliser recommendations are expressed as kg/ha MgO. Although grass growth is not susceptible to magnesium deficiency, it is important to maintain an adequate level of magnesium in grass herbage to help minimise the risk of livestock disorders such as hypomagnesaemia (grass staggers). Direct treatment may also be needed to protect stock from this condition.

Magnesium fertiliser is only likely to be justified for grass growth if the soil level is Index 0, when 85 kg/ha MgO should be applied. If there is a risk of hypomagnasaemia, larger amounts may be appropriate to maintain Index 2. Where soil magnesium reserves are small and liming is necessary, magnesian limestone should be used.

Sulphur

In many areas of England and Wales receiving only small amounts of sulphur from atmospheric deposition, experiments have shown that second and third silage cuts commonly give large responses to sulphur fertilisers. Grazed grass or first silage cuts are less likely to respond. Responses are most likely in areas where the mean annual sulphur deposition from the atmosphere is less than 30 kg/ha sulphur. (See map on page 26). Sandy or shallow soils of low organic matter are most prone, but deficiency is also common on some clay soils. Deficiency is less likely or will be less pronounced where organic manures have been used.

If atmospheric sulphur levels continue to decline, the extent of sulphur deficiency is likely to increase.

Soil analysis for sulphur is not recommended for assessing sulphur deficiency. Analysis of herbage samples provides a reliable means of determining if sulphur is deficient.

Note: Avoid applying excessive sulphur fertilizer as copper deficiency problems in livestock can be made worse.

Sodium

Sodium is essential for all animals. The sodium level in herbage is normally adequate for grazing livestock and application of sodium to pastures is unnecessary. However excess potash will depress the sodium content of grass. Mineral supplements may be required for some classes of livestock.

Farmyard Manures and Slurries

Where these materials are applied, allowance should be made for the available nutrients they contain. Fertiliser applications should be reduced accordingly—see Section 2

Trace elements

Grass production is not known to be limited by any trace element deficiency in England or Wales. However adequate levels of trace elements in grass

97

herbage are important to help achieve a correct and balanced nutrition of livestock. Copper, cobalt and selenium deficiencies are common in some grazing animals. Where a deficiency occurs, treatment of the animal with the appropriate trace element is usually the most effective means of control, though application of cobalt to grazing pastures can be effective.

RECOMMENDATIONS FOR GRASSLAND

Using the tables

For each of the main grass management systems, detailed recommendations for nitrogen, phosphate and potash are given in the following sections.

To find the correct recommendations it is important both to look in the table and to read the associated notes.

All recommendations are given in kilograms per hectare (kg/ha). The number of kilograms (kg) of the nutrient in a 50 kg bag of fertiliser is given by dividing the percentage of the nutrient by 2. For example, one 50 kg bag of a 20:10:10 NPK compound fertiliser will contain 10 kg of nitrogen, 5 kg of phosphate and 5 kg of potash. For conversion to imperial units see Appendix 3.

Example

A 1st cut silage crop (68–70D) is to be taken in a continuous grass field which has received 200 kg/ha nitrogen in the previous year (fertiliser plus animal manure N) and was cut and grazed.

Soil analysis had given a phosphorus Index of 2 and a potassium Index of 1. Using the table on page 95 the soil nitrogen supply is assessed as moderate.

The tables on pages 106 and 107 are consulted and the recommendation for this field is found to be 120 kg/ha nitrogen, 30 kg/ha of phosphate and 100 kg/ha of potash.

These rates can be applied by using straight fertilisers and/or organic manures or by choosing a compound fertiliser to give as near as possible the correct amounts. In most cases the first priority is to get the rate of nitrogen correct. Slight variation in the rates of phosphate or potash will have less effect on yield.

Grass Establishment—Spring sown

Nitrogen

	Soil Nitrogen Supply		
	Low	Moderate	High
		kg/ha	
	60	60	60

Phosphate and potash

	Index				
	0	1	2	3	Over 3
			kg/ha		
Phosphate	120	80	50	30	0
Potash	120	80	50	0	0

Do not apply nitrogen for autumn sown crops or for grass/clover swards where a high clover content is required.

Magnesium

For magnesium recommendations, see page 96.

Don't forget to deduct nutrients applied as organic manures—see page 8

99

Grass grazed by dairy or other cattle

Nitrogen rates are optimum levels for intensive systems. Lesser rates will be appropriate for less intensive grazing where less grass is required.

Continuous grazing

Nitrogen

	Soil Nitrogen Supply		
	Low	Moderate	High
		kg/ha	
1st Grazing[1]	60	60	60
2nd Grazing	75	60	60
3rd Grazing	75	60	50
4th Grazing	60	60	50
5th Grazing	60	60	40
Subsequent Grazings[2]	50	40	40

Rotational grazing

Nitrogen

	Soil Nitrogen Supply		
	Low	Moderate	High
		kg/ha	
1st Grazing[1]	60	60	60
2nd Grazing	60	60	50
3rd Grazing	60	50	40
4th Grazing	60	50	40
5th Grazing	50	50	40
6th Grazing	50	40	40
Subsequent Grazings[2]	40	30	30

Timing of applications

(1) Mid Feb–early March.
(2) Under intensive grazing systems application of nitrogen is not justified after mid-August. Later dressings will be used inefficiently and increase the risk of nitrate being leached over winter.

Don't forget to deduct nutrients applied as organic manures—see page 8.

Use the second grazing recommendation where grazing follows a silage or hay cut.

Prolonged dry weather will restrict grass growth. Reduce applications if drought persists.

Phosphate and Potash

	Index			
	0	1	2	over 2
Grazing			kg/ha	
Phosphate[3]	60	40	20	0
Potash[4]	60	30	0	0

Timing of Applications

(3) Apply for first grazing.
(4) Apply for 3rd grazing. At Index 0 divide equally between 1st and 3rd grazing.

Magnesium

For magnesium recommendations, see page 96.

Don't forget to deduct nutrients applied as organic manures—see page 8.

Grass grazed by sheep

Nitrogen rates are optimum levels for intensive systems. Lesser rates will be appropriate for less intensive grazing where less grass is required.

Nitrogen

	Soil Nitrogen Supply		
	Low	Moderate	High
	kg/ha		
1st Grazing[1]	60	60	60
2nd Grazing	60	60	50
3rd Grazing	60	50	40
4th Grazing	60	50	40
5th Grazing	50	40	30
Subsequent Grazings[2]	40	30	30

Timing of applications

(1) Mid Feb–early March.
(2) Under intensive grazing systems application of nitrogen is not justified after mid-August. Later dressings will be used inefficiently and increase the risk of nitrate being leached over winter.

Notes

Use the second grazing recommendations where grazing follows a silage or hay cut.

Prolonged dry weather will restrict grass growth. Reduce applications if drought persists.

Don't forget to deduct nutrients applied as organic manures—see page 8.

Phosphate and Potash

	Index			
	0	1	2	over 2
			kg/ha	
Phosphate[3]	60	40	20	0
Potash[4]	60	30	0	0

Timing of Applications

(3) Apply for first grazing.
(4) Apply for 3rd grazing. At Index 0 divide equally between 1st and 3rd grazing.

Magnesium

For magnesium recommendations, see page 96.

Don't forget to deduct nutrients applied as organic manures—see page 8.

Established grass/clover swards

Grazed swards

Nitrogen

	Soil Nitrogen Supply		
	Low	Moderate	High
		kg/ha	
Grazing[1],[2]	0	0	0
	0	0	0

Timing of applications

(1) Apply up to 50 kg/ha in mid Feb–early March if early grass growth is required.
(2) Apply up to 50 kg/ha in late August–early September if autumn grass is required.

Note

Clover is particularly sensitive to nitrogen application during the establishment stage. No nitrogen should be applied during this period.

Phosphate and Potash

	Index			
	0	1	2	Over 2
			kg/ha	
Phosphate[3]	60	40	20	0
Potash[4]	60	30	0	0

Timing of Applications

(3) Apply for 1st grazing.
(4) Apply for 3rd grazing. At Index 0 divide equally between 1st and 3rd grazing.

Note

For aftermath grazing apply 30 kg/ha potash per grazing for up to 2 grazings (not if Index 3 or over).

Don't forget to deduct nutrients applied as organic manures—see page 8.

Cut Swards

Nitrogen

	Soil Nitrogen Supply		
	Low	Moderate	High
		kg/ha	
1st Cut	0	0	0
2nd Cut	0	0	0

Phosphate and Potash

	Index				
	0	1	2	3	Over 3
			kg/ha		
1st Cut					
Phosphate	100	60	30	30	0
Potash	140[1]	100	60	30	0
2nd Cut					
Phosphate	50	30	30	0	0
Potash	120[1]	100	80	40	0

(1) Individual potash recommendations in excess of 100 kg/ha should be applied in the previous autumn.

Magnesium

For magnesium recommendations, see page 96.

Don't forget to deduct nutrients applied as organic manures—see page 8.

105

Grass cut for 68–70D silage
Nitrogen

	Soil Nitrogen Supply		
	Low	Moderate	High
		kg/ha	
1st cut[1]	150	120	120
2nd cut	110	100	100
3rd cut	80	80	60
4th cut	80	80	60

Timing of applications

(1) Apply 40 kg/ha nitrogen in mid Feb–early March with the remainder in late March–early April, at least 6 weeks before cutting.
Following early spring grazing, reduce the 1st cut recommendations for nitrogen by 25 kg/ha.

Don't forget to deduct nutrients applied as organic manures—see page 8

Phosphate and Potash

Crop	Index				
	0	1	2	3	Over 3
			kg/ha		
1st cut					
Phosphate	100	60	30	30	0
Potash[2]	140	100	60	30	0
2nd cut					
Phosphate	50	30	30	0	0
Potash[2]	120	100	80	40	0
3rd cut					
Phosphate	0	0	0	0	0
Potash	80	60	40	20	0
4th cut					
Phosphate	0	0	0	0	0
Potash	80	60	40	20	0

Timing of Applications

(2) Potash in excess of 100 kg/ha should be applied in the previous autumn.

Note

For aftermath grazing, apply 30 kg/ha potash per grazing for up to 2 grazings (not if Index 3 or over).

Magnesium and sulphur

For magnesium recommendations, see page 96.

Notes

For 1st cut silage, a sulphur fertiliser is recommended where deficiency is known to be severe. A sulphur fertiliser (38 kg/ha sulphur as SO_3 per cut) may be needed in areas of low atmospheric sulphur deposition (below 30 kg/ha sulphur—see map page 26) especially for 2nd and later cuts.

Don't forget to deduct nutrients applied as organic manures—see page 8

Grass cut for 64–67D silage

Nitrogen

	Soil Nitrogen Supply		
	Low	Moderate	High
		kg/ha	
1st cut[1]	150	150	120
2nd cut	120	100	100
3rd cut	100	80	80

Timing of application

(1) Apply 40 kg/ha nitrogen in mid Feb–early March with the remainder in late March–early April, at least 6 weeks before cutting. Following early spring grazing, reduce the 1st cut recommendations for N by 25 kg/ha.

Phosphate and Potash

Crop	Index				
	0	1	2	3	Over 3
			kg/ha		
1st cut					
Phosphate	100	60	30	30	0
Potash[2]	140	100	60	30	0
2nd cut					
Phosphate	50	30	30	0	0
Potash[2]	120	100	80	40	0
3rd cut					
Phosphate	0	0	0	0	0
Potash	80	60	40	20	0

Timing of Applications

(2) Potash in excess of 100 kg/ha should be applied in the previous autumn.

Note

For aftermath grazing, apply 30 kg/ha potash per grazing for up to 2 grazings (not if Index 3 or over).

Don't forget to deduct nutrients applied as organic manures—see page 8.

Magnesium and sulphur

For magnesium recommendations, see page 96.

Note

For 1st cut silage, a sulphur fertiliser may be needed where deficiency is known to be severe. A sulphur fertiliser (38 kg/ha sulphur as SO_3 per cut) may be needed in areas of low atmospheric sulphur deposition (below 30 kg/ha sulphur—see map page 26), especially for 2nd and later cuts.

Hay
Nitrogen

	Soil Nitrogen Supply		
	Low	Moderate	High
		kg/ha	
Each hay cut	90	70	60

Phosphate and Potash

	Index				
	0	1	2	3	Over 3
			kg/ha		
Phosphate	100	60	30	30	0
Potash	100	80	60	30	0

Magnesium

For magnesium recommendations, see page 96.

Don't forget to deduct nutrients applied as organic manures—see page 8.

Appendix 1   Classification of Soil Analysis Results for Samples Analysed by Standard Procedures

(See MAFF Reference Book 427, The Analysis of Agricultural Materials)

Index	Phosphorus (mg/l)	Potassium (mg/l)	Magnesium (mg/l)
0	0–9	0–60	0–25
1	10–15	61–120	26–50
2	16–25	121–240	51–100
3	26–45	241–400	101–175
4	46–70	401–600	176–250
5	71–100	601–900	251–350
6	101–140	901–1500	351–600
7	141–200	1501–2400	601–1000
8	201–280	2401–3600	1001–1500
9	over 280	over 3600	over 1500

Appendix 2   Soil Types

Sandy

Soils which are sand or loamy sand to 40 cm depth and are sandy to 100 cm. Soils which are sandy loam to 40 cm only are classified as 'Other Mineral'.

Shallow

Mineral soils over chalk, limestone or other rock in which the parent material is within 40 cm of the soil surface. Sandy soils developed over sandstone should be regarded as sandy.

Clay

Soils with predominantly clay or clay loam topsoils overlying clay subsoils.

Deep Silty

Soils of sandy silt loam, silt loam to silty clay loam texture to 100 cm depth.

Other Mineral Soils

Mineral soils that do not fall into any of the categories shown in the tables.

Organic Soils

Soils that are predominantly mineral but contain between 6 and 20% organic matter. These can be distinguished by darker colouring that stains the fingers black or grey and gives the soil a silty feel.

Peaty Soils

Soils that contain more than 20% organic matter derived from sedge or similar plant material.

Appendix 3 Metric-Imperial Conversion

10 tonnes/ha	=	4 tons/acre
100 kg/ha	=	80 units/acre
1 kg/tonne	=	2 units/ton
10 cm	=	4 inches
1 m³	=	220 gallons
1 m³/ha	=	90 gallons/acre

1 unit = ½ kg

2.47 acres = 1 ha

(2.5)